Nurse Executive Review Study Guide

Nurse Executive Certification Resource and Practice Test Questions Book for the Nurse Executive Exam

FREE STRESS RELIEF BALL FROM TRIVIUM TEST PREP

Dear Customer,

Thank you for purchasing from Trivium Test Prep! Whether you're looking to join the military, get into college, or advance your career, we're honored to be a part of your journey.

To show our appreciation (and to help you relieve a little of that test-prep stress), we're offering a **FREE 5-Star Stress Relief Ball from Trivium Test Prep**. All we ask is that you email us your feedback and describe your experience with our product. Amazing, awful, or just so-so: we want to hear your thoughts!

To receive your **FREE 5-Star Stress Relief Ball from Trivium Test Prep**, please email us at 5star@triviumtestprep.com. Include "Free 5 Star" in the subject line and the following information in your email:

1. The title of the product you purchased.

2. Your rating from 1 – 5 (with 5 being the best).

3. Your feedback about the product, including how our materials helped you meet your goals and ways in which we can improve our products.

4. Your full name and shipping address so we can send your FREE 5-Star Stress Relief Ball.

If you have any questions or concerns please feel free to contact me directly.

Thank you, and good luck with your studies!

Alyssa Wagoner
Quality Control
alyssa.wagoner@triviumtestprep.com

Table of Contents

Introduction

Congratulations! By reading this book, it means you have decided to advance your career in the medical field by earning your Nurse Executive certification. Before we get started, let's review some of the basic information. You are likely already familiar with this exam, the eligibility requirements, and so on, so we will keep it brief.

About the Exam

The Nurse Executive exam is created and administered by the ANCC, or American Nurses Credentialing Center. The credential you will be awarded upon successful completion of the exam is referred to by the ANCC as "NE-BC". The actual exam is 175 questions (150 are scored, 25 are "pre-test" that are not scored) and you will have 3.5 hours to complete the entire test.

Eligibility Requirements

Per the ANCC, applicants for the NE-BC credential must:
- Hold a Bachelor's or higher degree in the field or nursing
- Hold a current, active RN license within a state or territory of the United States or the professional, legally recognized equivalent in another country.
- Have held a mid-level administrative or higher position such as a supervisor or director. Alternatively, have held a faculty position teaching graduate nursing students.
- Have completed 30 hours of continuing education in nursing administration within the last 3 years.

Applying for the Exam

You may apply by mail, or you can register online. In either case, you will need to find the ANCC website at www.nursecredentialing.org , find your certification under the "certification". Once you arrive at the introduction page for the Nurse Executive page, you will see the instructions for completing the application online. If you want to do it by mail, you will need to download the application from online and then print and mail it in. If you have questions, you can always call their customer care team at 1-800-284-2378. There is a $395 fee to sit for this exam, or $270 if you are an ANCC member.

Preparing for the Exam

Obviously, you are already off to a great start by reading this book! However, there are of course additional resources you should use as well. When you visit the ANCC website to apply for the exam, be sure to look through the free resources available there. You can see an outline or "blueprint" of the exam, which is very helpful to familiarize yourself with the general concepts you'll see on the test. This won't provide any detail about the concepts, so it's not useful for in-depth studying like you will get in this book, but is certainly a good idea to be familiar with the outline of the exam. The more you know about and are familiar with the exam beforehand, the better you'll do. They also provide a few sample questions, so is a good place to get an initial assessment of your current knowledge if you like (we have a lot of practice questions in this book too of course). Finally, if you find yourself struggling with specific concepts, the ANCC has a list of references you can find to get very in-depth reviews. There are 25 different resources listed, so you obviously would never have time to read through everything, but is good to know about in case you need it later.

Chapter 1: Structures and Processes

This chapter covers the concepts and elements of structures and processes including human capital management, financial management, and health and public policy.

HUMAN CAPITAL MANAGEMENT

Human capital management (HCM) approaches employee staffing with the view that people are assets (human capital). The employee's value can be quantified, and the future value of an employee can be increased through investment. Clearly defined and well-communicated performance expectations of employees is an asset of an institution that supports HCM. Management is responsible for rating and rewarding each employee and also holds the employee accountable for achieving certain goals, supporting continued improvement, and innovating.

HCM is a part of *enterprise resource planning* (ERP), which involves employee records. The employee documentation offers managers the necessary information to make decisions based on factual data. Software can automate and streamline many daily recordkeeping procedures and processes and provide a framework for human resource staff to manage administration, benefits, and payroll. Additionally, HCM software can create and map out succession planning and record compliance with industry regulations and government standards and personnel actions.

Human Capital Assessment and Accountability Framework (HCAAF)

The Human Capital Assessment and Accountability Framework (HCAAF) is a set of specific guidelines with merit system principles, veterans' preference rules, and other civil service rules, laws, and regulations. The five human capital systems are distinct, but also interrelated in their goal of producing a better workforce. They include:

- Strategic Alignment
- Talent Management
- Results-Oriented Performance Culture
- Accountability
- Leadership and Knowledge Management

The Strategic Alignment System

The Strategic Alignment System focuses on aligning a human capital strategy with organizational objectives, mission, and goals. This system should be directed by senior management, usually the Chief Human Capital Officer (CHCO). The standard of this system is integrated into its performance plans, strategic plans, and budgets. Each system is based on critical success factors, which are the areas where human capital managers and agencies must focus to achieve a system's standard for success and operate efficiently and effectively. The Strategic Alignment System is comprised of the following critical success factors:

- Workforce planning
- Human capital planning
- Human resources as a strategic partner
- Human capital knowledge sharing
- Human capital best practices

The Leadership and Knowledge Management System

The Leadership and Knowledge Management System aims to identify and address organization leadership competencies in order to assure continued leadership and share knowledge across the agency. Agency managers can effectively manage personnel and achieve a learning environment that allows for improved performance and provides a means of sharing critical knowledge across the organization. This system is includes the following critical success factors:

- Knowledge management
- Integrity and inspiring employee commitment
- Change management
- Leadership succession management
- Continuous learning

Federal and State Laws

The Federal Workforce Flexibility Act of 2004

The federal government focuses on good management and the concept that people are central to delivery of services to the American public. The Federal Workforce Flexibility Act of 2004 added many strategies that support human capital management.

The underlying expectation for all of these changes is strategic capital management to ensure that all human resource activity contributes directly to achieving the government's results and are rewarded.

Family and Medical Leave Act (FMLA)[1]

The Family and Medical Leave Act (FMLA) entitles eligible employees of certain covered employers to take unpaid, job-protected leave for specified medical and family reasons with continuation of group health insurance coverage.

Covered Employers

The FMLA applies only to certain employers. These include:
- Private-sector employers with 50 or more employees in 20 or more work weeks in the current or preceding calendar year including a successor or joint employer in interest to a covered employer
- Public agencies (local, state, and federal) regardless of the number of employees
- Public or private elementary or secondary schools regardless of the number of employees

Eligible Employees

An eligible employee is someone who:
- Works for a covered employer
- Has worked for the employer for at least 12 months
- Has at least 1,250 hours of service for the employer during that 12 month period
- Works at a location where the employer has at least 50 employees

Eligible Employee Benefits

Eligible employees are entitled to 12 work weeks of leave in a one-year period for the following cases:
- Birth of a child and care for the newborn during this time frame
- Care for a child, spouse, or parent with a serious health condition
- Care for an adopted child or a child in newly placed foster care
- Serious health condition that makes the employee unable to work
- Qualifying need arising from the fact that the employee's spouse, son, daughter, or parent is a covered military member on "covered active duty"

---

[1] "Family and Medical Leave Act," U.S. Department of Labor, Wage and Hour Division, accessed October 27, 2015, http://www.dol.gov/whd/fmla/

Eligible employees are entitled to 26 work weeks of leave during a one-year period for the following cases:

- Care for a covered service member with a serious injury or illness if the eligible employee is the service member's spouse, son, daughter, parent, or next-of-kin

Employee Notice Requirements under the FMLA

Covered employers must:

- Post a notice explaining rights and responsibilities under the FMLA (and may be subject to a civil money penalty of up to $110 for willful failure to post)
- Include information about the FMLA in employee handbooks or provide information to new employees upon hire
- Acquire knowledge that leave may be for a FMLA-qualifying reason and provide employee with notice concerning his/her eligibility for FMLA leave and his/her rights and responsibilities under the FMLA
- Notify employees whether leave is designated as FMLA leave and the amount of leave that will be deducted from the employee's FMLA entitlement

Employer Notice Requirements under the FMLA

When an employee requests FMLA leave due to a serious health condition related to himself/herself or a family member, the employer can require certification from a healthcare professional to support the leave. An employer may also require second and third medical opinions and periodic recertification of the serious health condition.

It is unlawful for any employer to interfere with, restrain, or deny the exercise of or the attempt to exercise any right provided by the FMLA. It is also unlawful for an employer to discharge or discriminate against any individual for opposing any practice or because of involvement in any proceeding related to the FMLA.

Americans with Disabilities Act (ADA)[2]

President George H.W. Bush signed the Americans with Disabilities Act (ADA) into law in 1990. This act ensures that qualified individuals with disabilities enjoy the same employment opportunities as those without physical or mental disability. According to the ADA, the term disability has three distinct definitions:

---

[2] "The Americans with Disabilities Act of 1990 and Revised ADA Regulations Implementing Title II and III," U.S. Department of Justice, Civil Rights Division, accessed October 27, 2015, http://www.ada.gov/2010_regs.htm.

- A physical or mental impairment that substantially limits one or more major life activities
- A record of such impairment
- Being regarded as having such an impairment

Five Titles of the ADA

The Equal Employment Opportunity Commission (EEOC) organized five titles of the ADA:

- Title I: Employment – This prohibits employers from discriminating on the basis of a disability and applies to all aspects of employment.

- Title II: Public Service – This requires public entities employed in public transportation services to provide accessible services to disabled individuals.

- Title III: Public Accommodations and Services Operated by Private Entities – This prohibits discrimination by private entities such as restaurants, lodging, and educational institutes in places of public accommodations.

- Title IV: Telecommunications Relay Services – This requires carriers of telephonic services to provide equal communication opportunities to people with disabilities.

- Title V: Provisions – This provides certain provisions such as attorney fees, prohibition against employer retaliation, and state immunity.

Reasonable Accommodation

According to the EEOC, reasonable accommodation means modifications:

- To the job application process that allow a qualified individual with a disability to be considered for a certain position
- To the work environment circumstances, or manner under which the position is held, that allow a qualified person with a disability to perform the necessary work functions
- That enable an employee with a disability to profit from the same privileges and benefits as those without a disability

Fair Labor Standards Act (FLSA)[3]

The Fair Labor Standards Act (FLSA) establishes minimum wage, record keeping, overtime pay, and young employment standards for full-time and part-time workers in the private sector and in local, state, and federal governments. This act covers more than 85% of all non-supervisory employees. The FLSA includes certain regulations regarding waiting time, on-call time, preparatory and concluding activities, and attendance to meetings, lectures, training programs, and other employer-related functions. The Wage and Hour Division regulates FLSA for local and state government employment, private employment, and federal employees of the U.S. Postal Service, Tennessee Valley Authority, Postal Rate Commission, and Library of Congress.

Record Keeping

Under the FLSA, an employer must keep a record of hours worked each workday and each workweek. With time clocks, rounding to the nearest fraction of an hour is allowed based on the fact that this averages out over a certain time period so that employees are fully paid for all hours worked. For employees 16 years of age and older, the FLSA does not limit the number of hours in a day or days in a week (including overtime hours) an employee must work. The FLSA does not require that employers give breaks or meal periods to workers, but some states implement these requirements.

Hours Worked and Minimum Wage

The FLSA sets a *minimum wage* below which no covered employee may be legally employed, but the law sets a maximum number of hours in a workweek. A workweek is a regularly reoccurring period of 168 hours during seven consecutive 24-hour periods. Hours worked includes all the time an employee must remain on duty on the employer's premises or at the designated worksite and all the time an employee must work for the employer.

Overtime Pay

Certain employees are exempt from *overtime pay* and minimum wage requirements. The three main "white-collar" exemptions include executive, professional, and administrative employees. Others who are subject to exemptions include apprentices, students, and individuals subject to child labor regulations. Unless exempted, employees

---

[3] "Compliance Assistance – Wage and the Fair Labor Standards Act," U.S. Department of Labor, Wage and Hour Division, accessed October 27, 2015, http://www.dol.gov/whd/flsa/.

covered by the FLSA must receive overtime pay for all hours in excess of 40 hours worked in a work week at a minimum rate of time and one-half of their regular rate of pay.

Wage and Hour Laws

The three most common violations by employers involve compensation, record keeping, and exemption status. Certain important legislation regarding these areas includes:

- FLSA Child Labor Provisions – The child labor provisions establish the basic minimum age for employment, which is 16 years. However, employment of 14 and 15-year-old youths is allowed for certain occupations and under specific guidelines.

- FLSA Amendments of 1989 – The U.S. Department of Labor's Wage and Hour Division implemented amendments to the FLSA that require employees lacking basic skills to receive additional remedial training in addition to their 40-hour workweek.

- Equal Pay Act of 1963 – The Equal Pay Act (EPA) requires that men and women performing equal work receive equal pay. This act prohibits discrimination based on gender regarding compensation for work services.

Equal Employment Opportunity Commission (EEOC)[4]

The Equal Employment Opportunity Commission (EEOC) enforces Title VII of the Civil Rights Act of 1964, the Age Discrimination in Employment Act of 1967 (ADEA), and the Rehabilitation Act of 1973. Equal employment laws involve various aspects of discrimination due to color, race, religion, age, national origin, gender, pregnancy, sexual orientation, and sexual harassment. The EEOC governs the act's interpretation and settles disputes regarding discrimination. This organization attempts to reach an agreement between the employee and employer through persuasion and conciliation. If an agreement is not reached, the EEOC can bring a civil action against an employer on behalf of the person or persons claiming to be aggrieved.

Civil Rights Act of 1964

Under the Civil Rights Act, employers cannot discriminate against an employee based on factors not related to job qualifications such as age, sexual preference, religion, race,

---

[4] "Employees & Job Applicants," U.S. Equal Employment Opportunity Commission, accessed October 27, 2015, http://www.eeoc.gov/employees/index.cfm.

gender, and national origin. Also, it promotes employment due to merit and/or ability. This law corrects injustices and bias through affirmative action and other mechanisms. This permits employers from "screening out" certain people who are qualified for employment. One exception to this act is bonafide occupational qualification (BFOQ), where certain challenges are more difficult or unattainable due to age. BFOQs include weight-bearing and mobility issues such as stairs, lifting, and other physical challenges.

Employers who are not subject to anti-discrimination laws include:
- Those with 15 or fewer employees
- Joint labor-management committees that control job training programs
- Labor organizations
- Independent contractors
- Unpaid volunteers
- Non-citizens employed overseas by U.S. employers

Age Discrimination in Employment Act of 1967 (ADEA)

To promote employment of older people based on their ability, Congress enacted the Age Discrimination in Employment Act (ADEA) in 1967. This act prevents arbitrary age discrimination in regards to employment and helps employers and workers to discover ways to solve problems arising from the impact of age on employment. Individuals protected by ADEA include those between the ages of 40 and 70 years.

Rehabilitation Act of 1973

The Rehabilitation Act of 1973 ensures that qualified individuals with handicaps are not excluded from participation in various programs and activities or denied benefits from an employer. This regulation prohibits the discrimination against an employee with a disability who is otherwise qualified. A qualified handicapped person is someone who can perform the main functions of the job with reasonable accommodations.

Affirmative Action

Affirmative action (also called employment equity) promotes equal opportunity and ethnic diversity in the workplace, in public contracting, in education, and in health programs. Affirmative action programs are typically formed for racial/ethnic minorities, disabled individuals, women, and those who have served or are serving in the military.

Occupational Safety and Health Administration (OSHA)[5]

The Occupational Safety and Health Administration (OSHA) covers any employer who operates or engages in a business that affects commerce. This administration requires that the employer furnishes for each employee a place of work that is free from recognized hazards that have or can result in serious physical harm or death. The Occupational Safety and Health Act of 1970 is broadly written federal legislation, which is modeled after the California OSHA programs. Since its inception, this act has been amended several times.

OSHA is authorized to conduct workplace inspection on each business that is covered by the OSHA act. The U.S. Department of Labor is the federal department that governs OSHA and allows OSHA to conduct an inspection at the request of an employer or in response to an employee complaint. The reports that are considered top priority are those that indicate imminent dangers, fatalities, or accidents that send three or more workers to the hospital. The Site-Specific Targeting Program focuses on employers that report increased illness rates or high injury percentages. OSHA also has special emphasis programs that focus on hazardous work such as mechanical power press equipment and trenching.

Record Keeping

To verify compliance with the OSHA Act, OSHA requires employers to keep certain records. OSHA supplies certain forms to employers available on the OSHA website. Employers with 11 or more employees must keep records of work-related illnesses and injuries. This encompasses around 1.5 million companies and organizations, or 20% of the establishments covered by OSHA. Workplaces that are exempt from record keeping include low-hazard industries such as finance, retail, insurance, real estate, and service.

OSHA Statistics

According to current statistics reported by OSHA, workplace injuries and illness rates have declined by 67%, and occupational deaths have decreased by more than 65%. Assisted by the efforts of state partners, employers, safety and health professionals, advocates, and unions, OSHA has had a significant effect on workplace safety. Since enactment, U.S. employment has almost doubled.

---

[5] "Workers," U.S. Department of Labor, Occupational Safety & Health Administration, accessed October 27, 2015, https://www.osha.gov/workers/index.html.

OSHA Cooperative Plans

Five types of cooperative plans offered by OSHA to increase workplace safety are:

- VPP – A reduction of lost workdays increases worker protection, decreases business costs, improves employee morale, and enhances productivity. Worksite Voluntary Protection Programs (VPP) document lost workday cases of around 70%, which is lower than their industry averages. These results were verified by OSHA.

- Alliance Program – The Alliance Program works in conjunction with several other organizations involved with workplace health and safety including unions, employers, trade groups, professional organizations, and education institutions.

- OSPP – The Strategic Partnership Program (OSPP) is for employers with special interest and experience in job safety and health who also have a commitment to improving workplace safety.

- Challenge Program – OSHA Challenge Program provides interested employers and employees the opportunity to gain assistance in improving their health and safety management systems. This program uses a three-stage process to prevent injuries, illnesses, and fatalities.

- SHARP – Safety and Health Achievement Recognition Program (SHARP) offers employers that have a full on-site consultation visit who meet certain requirements to be recognized for exemplary management systems. Worksites that receive the SHARP recognition are exempt from OSHA inspections during the valid inspection period.

Workers' Compensation

With the Workers' Compensation law, an employee who becomes ill or is injured on the job or from a condition caused by the worksite is compensated for that incident. This includes reimbursement for hospital costs and medical care. These state statutes establish an employer's liability for workers' job related injuries and illnesses. Workers' compensation includes absolute liability for medical coverage, costs of rehabilitation, payment for permanent injury, and a percentage of wages or salary.

Labor Relations

Collective Bargaining

Collective bargaining is a negotiated agreement between an employer and a labor union that defines the terms of employment for workers who belong to that labor union. The term "collective" shows that agreements cover a defined population within an organization and are not individualized. This agreement includes provisions that relate to vacation time, work hours, working conditions, wages, and health insurance benefits. Most collective bargaining agreements relative to registered nurses in the U.S. are negotiated through the labor arm of the American Nurses Association (ANA). The exceptions to this are the California and Massachusetts Nurses Associations.

Negotiations and Contracts

Labor unions and management have a mutual obligation to bargain in a good faith effort, called *negotiation,* to reach an agreement related to the conditions of employment affecting employees represented by this organization. *Conditions of employment* broadly involve personnel practices and policies and matters affecting work conditions. However, race, gender, religion, disability, age, and national origin are all matters that are excluded as conditions of employment under current federal law.

A *contract* is a legally qualified agreement for a particular benefit of two or more people, which is a voluntary act. Many states accept verbal contracts as legal contracts under this concept. Nursing executives need to negotiate contracts in the employment setting because positions can be eliminated or restructured in the healthcare environment. A contract will protect the nursing professional financially and will secure job status. Contracts define the responsibilities and liabilities of employees, contractors, and/or other service providers.

Grievances and Arbitrations

A *grievance* in a collective bargaining agreement covers any complaint by:
- Any employee concerning a matter associated with employment
- Any labor organization regarding a matter associated to the employment of any employee

- Any employee, labor organization, or agency concerning the effect, interpretation, or claim of breach of a collective bargaining agreement or violation

The *negotiated grievance procedure* is a dispute-resolution system. This method is established by the labor union and management to determine problems and solve them quickly and fairly. A negotiated grievance procedure must be established for all collective bargaining agreements. Under these procedures, labor unions can present and process union or employee grievances.

Any negotiated grievance that is not resolved by the grievance process is subject to binding arbitration. *Arbitration* is a process where a final and binding award is given by an arbitrator. The *arbitrator* is chosen by the labor union and management to hear and review the evidence. The labor union or management has 30 days to file an exception to an arbitrator's award. The Federal Labor Relations Authority reviews the award to determine if it violates rules, regulations, and/or laws on grounds similar to those of federal courts in the private sector of labor-management relations.

National Labor Relations Act (NLRA)[6]
The National Labor Relations Board (NLRB) is an independent federal agency created by Congress to regulate and administer the National Labor Relations Act (NLRA). Also known as the Wagner Act of 1935, this act is the primary law governing relations between employers and labor unions in the private sector. The law protects workers from unfair labor practices and requires that employers recognize and bargain collectively with the labor union. The NLRA essentially guarantees employees the right to:
- Self-organize
- Form, join, or assist labor organizations
- Engage in activities for the purpose of collective bargaining

Resource Utilization and Benefits

Employee Assistance
An *employee assistance program* (EAP) provides a service to help organizations, managers, and employees meet life challenges and remain productive and healthy.

---

[6] "Who We Are," National Labor Relations Board, accessed October 27, 2015, https://www.nlrb.gov/who-we-are.

An EAP gives employees short-term counseling and referral for issues that could negatively impact work ability. It also addresses employee concerns during the counseling sessions and refers employees to appropriate community resources, support groups, and counselors.

Employee Counseling

Commonly addressed issues for employees include:

- Life challenges – Mental disorders, drug and/or alcohol use and abuse, and eating disorders

- Life changes – New baby, new job, divorce, aging parents, retirement, and grief and loss

- Job stress and burnout

- Coping – Dealing with difficult people or situations

Commonly addressed issues for nurse executives and organizations include:

- Coaching – How to refer employees to EAP, how to handle difficult employees, ways to be a better manager, and how to have performance conversations with staff

- Counseling – Assistance with how to manage life challenges and changes

- Performance – Support for employees and managers in their efforts to perform jobs and achieve goals

- Stress management – Helps executives and managers prepare to recover from any traumatic events

Culture and Structure

Corporate Culture and Climate

Corporate culture is characterized as an organization's or facility's system of shared values, beliefs, and actions that guides member behavior. Also called *corporate climate*, corporate culture is a powerful force that defines the characteristics of the workplace and helps guide new members. Awareness of an organizational culture before accepting a position allows potential employees to determine if their values align with those of the organization. Corporate culture rarely changes in response to a single individual or small group of people.

Culture Types

The three main types of culture are:

- Autocratic – The *autocratic* culture is characterized as a "top-down" concept, with decisions made at the executive level and then announced to the workers. Managers and supervisors must enforce the decisions and help staff accept various decisions and changes. Techniques of an autocratic organization include coercion, direction of actions, and threats of punishment. In many organizations, the success of the facility depends on autocracy.

- Bureaucratic – A *bureaucratic* culture relies on rules, regulations, procedures, and policies. All companies use policies and procedures, but with a bureaucratic organization, rules are central to structure. Many government agencies are classified as bureaucratic.

- Participative – A *participative* culture is characterized as openness to recommendations and suggestions from all levels within the facility for the purpose of decision making. Employees are often disappointed when the final decision is contrary or different from their given input. In this culture, nurse executives must let employees know in advance how their suggestions and recommendations will be used.

Organizational Structure

Chain of Command

The *chain of command* refers to the command line that exists from the top to the bottom of an organization. Each unit within the organization is linked to another. The chain of command allows for a smooth exchange of information. Each subsequent layer of the chain of command must report to the one immediately above it.

Span of Control

The *span of control* is the scope of responsibility of a given manager or supervisor. With this concept, responsibilities and tasks are divided to accomplish goals without placing a burden on any one unit or person within the organization.

Organizational Chart

An *organizational chart* reflects the principles of the chain of command and span of control, with each unit or person connected to another. This chart clarifies relationships between individuals and functions within an organization, and it is used to show formal relationships or connections among groups or people within an organization. These charts illustrate how services such as location (3 West, 4 South, 5 North), service line (oncology, orthopedics, cardiology), and service delivery (cardiac care, ambulatory care, surgery) are arranged within a facility.

FINANCIAL MANAGEMENT

Financial management is vital to the health and stability of a healthcare facility. The organization must employ executives and managers who understand basic financial principles, key accounting principles, resource management, payment options, principles of the nursing workload, budgeting, and strategies for cost containment.

Basic Financial and Accounting Principles

Revenue Cycle
Revenue is the total amount of income expected during a specific time duration. This revenue is an income source that includes reimbursement from patient care, membership dues from direct-member health maintenance organizations (HMOs), and sales of goods or products. Nurse executive do not typically have direct control over revenue; several cost centers are allocated a percentage of anticipated or actual revenue.

Staffing
Staffing distribution determines the allocated number of personnel for every shift. Many healthcare facilities require 40% for day shift, 35% for evening shift, and 25% for night shift. The *staffing mix* is the proportion of different types of personnel on a shift. For example, one shift may require 40% RNs, 40% LPNs, and 20% CNAs. The staff mix often skews toward a high percentage of RNs, depending on the philosophy of the facility. Also called *staffing ratio*, staffing mix is often determined by legislation, particularly for intensive care units and emergency departments. This RN ratio legislation is relative in many states and will likely continue in the future.

Expenses

The *expense budget* contains both non-salary and salary items. A responsibility of nurse executives is to manage the expenditures of the cost centers assigned to them, (an outflow of resources). Some facilities also require the manager to handle a profit center, (an inflow of cash). Costs are either variable or fixed. *Fixed costs* are constant costs to the facility that do not change regardless of fluctuating activity levels, such as insurance premiums or fees. *Variable costs* experience fluctuation based on either an external or internal influence (e.g. patient acuity, staff mix, census, or product cost (Rundio & Wilson, 2010).

Productivity

Productivity, in an organizational or industrial context, describes the relationship between *inputs* (resources used to produce outputs) and *outputs* (products or services delivered). There are two models of productivity that are specific to nursing: the industrial model and the systems framework. The *industrial model* is a ratio that measures work output to work input and is considered representative of efficiency. For example, nursing costs per unit of service illustrates the principles of the industrial model. The *systems framework* involves both efficiency and efficacy, with efficiency including nursing output and efficacy including quality and appropriateness (Rundio & Wilson, 2010).

Depreciation

Depreciation is an income tax deduction that is an annual allowance for the wear-and-tear or deterioration of the property. It allows a taxpayer to recover the costs or other aspects of specific property. Many types of tangible property such as machinery, equipment, buildings, furniture, and vehicles can be depreciated. Intangible property including copyrights, patents, and computer software is also depreciable (Internal Revenue Service, 2012).

The requirements for depreciation set by the Internal Revenue Service (2012) include:
- The property must have a determinable useful life of one year or more.
- The taxpayer must own the property, and he/she can depreciate any capital improvements from leased property.
- The taxpayer must use the property for business or in an income-producing aspect. If the property is used for personal purposes as well as for business, the taxpayer can deduct depreciation based only on the business use.

Return on Investment (ROI)

A *business plan* uses economic justification to show chief financial officers and elected board officials the necessary information. This plan helps decision makers decide what to do and if the choice is right. A popular economic calculation to show an investment is the *return on investment* (ROI). The ROI is found by calculating the most tangible financial benefits or gains expected from a given project compared to the costs for implementing a program or solution. While similar to the ROI, the *cost benefit analysis* (CBA) is more comprehensive than the ROI in that it quantifies both intangible (soft) and tangible benefits and costs.

The formula for calculating ROI is: $ROI = \frac{Net\ Benefits}{Total\ Cost}$. This equation illustrates a ratio of a project's expected financial benefits or gains to its total overall cost. The net benefits are the difference between total benefits and the total cost, an incremental financial gain or loss value. If a project costs $40,000 and demonstrates $20,000 in net benefits, the ROI calculation would be: $ROI = \frac{\$20,000}{\$40,000}$. In order for a program to appear fiscally attractive, it requires ROI ratio greater than zero.

Cost-Benefit Analysis

The *cost-benefit ratio* is the proportion between the activity's benefit value and activity's cost value, expressed as a fraction. The activity is considered economically beneficial, when the ratio is greater than 1, because the benefits outweigh the costs. In *cost-benefit analysis*, the relative value of an intervention is assessed with predetermined criteria. One example of this type of analysis is determining whether providing a skilled nursing facility is more or less cost effective than offering home care. Nurse executives can address complex problems quickly and cost-effectively with biomathematical modeling, whereas clinical trials or observational studies do not allow for such expedience.

The *cost-benefit analysis* predicts a net value of an organization's planned action. This analysis identifies, quantifies, and sums all benefits (positive factors). Then, it finds, quantifies, and deducts all negative factors (costs). The difference between the two values indicates whether a planned action is profitable. By analyzing with this method, organizations can detect actual, quantitative savings; soft dollar savings; and cost avoidance, which is the elimination of future costs such as equipment leases and overtime pay. Additionally, the time value of money is central to the cost-benefit analysis concept. An amount of money has more value today than the same amount will have in the future. A cost-benefit analysis allows for this difference by accurately quantifying the costs and benefits of the action.

Resource-Based Relative Value Scale (RBRVS) System

Medicare established a standardized payment schedule for physicians and implemented the Resource-Based Relative Value Scale (RBRVS) system in 1992. The resource costs needed to provide services determine the payments for said services. There are three aspects of the cost of service: practice expense, professional liability insurance, and physician work. The Centers for Medicare and Medicaid Services (CMS) set a conversion factor, a monetary amount that is multiplied with the costs of services to calculate the payments. In 2002, the CMS transitioned to resource-based practice expense values for each CPT code.

Resource Management and Payment Options

Fee for Service

Fee for service reimbursement is the standard payment option. However, newer methods of payment may dominate physician and healthcare facility reimbursement in the future. The fee for service payment method differs from payment for goods or services in other sectors of the economy due to price. With healthcare, the amount paid for services is often negotiated between the provider and the payer (American Medical Association, 2013).

Pay for Performance

A *pay for performance* (PFP) approach compensates healthcare facilities and physicians based on performance. The healthcare insurer or other payer measures performance on organizational data, such as patient satisfaction and the cost and quality of care. The payer rates the physician or facility according to their own criteria (American Medical Association, 2013).

Pay for Coordination

The *pay for coordination* (PFC) model of payment applies to specified care coordination services by certain types of providers such as home healthcare. This model's benefits are linked with the concept of paying for care coordination, which involves support services and other work that is not available under a fee for service model. Those benefits improve the physician-patient relationship and communication between patients and healthcare providers. This model also reduces the delivery of unnecessary care such as duplicate tests and futile care.

Bundled Payments

With the *bundled payment* method, two or more providers are covered by a single bundled payment, if they both administered care of a single episode during a certain time period. Common examples include global payments for surgery, obstetric care, and emergency services. These bundles include a broad array of services.

Principles of Nursing Workload

Full-Time Equivalent (FTE)

The amount of time that a full-time employee would work each week is the *Full-time equivalent* (FTE). A 40-hour workweek is equivalent to five 8-hour workdays of staffing, which has value of 1.0. One FTE could equal 2 part-time employees, each working 20 hours per week, or one full-time employee working 40 hours per week. The FTE of a position with more than five days or 40 hours is greater than 1.0 for that particular post, such as occurs in nursing care. A 7-day coverage where 8 hours each day must be covered would equal a 1.4 FTE (56 / 40 = 1.4). Therefore, that position requires more than one person to cover it.

Hours Per Patient Day (HPPD)

The hours of nursing care each patient requires each day is considered the *hours per patient day* (HPPD). This value is calculated by dividing total production hours by the number of patients.

Volume Indicators

Volume is a significant tool for predicting profitability as a large proportion of facility and healthcare provider costs are fixed. Two *volume indicators* include the average daily census and occupancy rate.

- Average Daily Census – The *average daily census* measures inpatient volume based on the number of occupied beds (patients). To determine this value, divide the total annual patient days by 365. A higher ADC increases profitability because the fixed costs are spread between more patients. This measure is often called census.

$$\text{Average Daily Census} = \frac{Total\ Annual\ Patient\ Days}{365}$$

- Occupancy Rate – The calculation for the *occupancy rate* is illustrated in the equation below. Occupancy rate demonstrates inpatient volume as a percentage of the number of occupied beds. Unless the occupancy rate is unmanageable high, a high occupancy rate typically lends itself to more profitability. To raise this rate, healthcare facilities can increase admissions, decrease the number of beds, or increase the length of patient stay. This measure is often referred to as occupancy.

$$\text{Occupancy Rate} = \frac{Total\ Annual\ Patient\ Days \times 100}{Number\ of\ Beds \times 365}$$

Profitability Indicators

The profitability assessment of the financial ratio analysis is explained by *profitability indicators*. Two of these are:

- Profit per Inpatient Discharge – The *profit per inpatient discharge* measures the amount of profit earned because of inpatient discharge. Negative numbers represent low values, and can be attributed to low inpatient reimbursement or high inpatient costs or both. The lack of inpatient profitability can lead to serious financial difficulties.

$$\text{Profit per Discharge} = \frac{Inpatient\ Revenue - Inpatient\ Operating\ Expenses}{Total\ Discharges}$$

- Profit per Inpatient Discharge (Adjusted) – This is the value adjusted for wage rate and case mix. It is the represented in the formula below:

$$\text{Adjusted Profit per Discharge} = \frac{Inpatient\ Revenue - Inpatient\ Operating\ Expenses}{Total\ Discharges \times Wage\ Index \times Case\ Mix\ Index}$$

Acuity and Workload Index

The *workload index* is weighted statistics that reflect production hours, census, and the *acuity* level of patients. This index often functions as a baseline for improving productivity. To get the workload index, you multiply the *acuity index* by the workload units and divide by the number of production hours.

$$\text{Workload Index} = \frac{Acuity\ Index \times Workload\ Units}{Number\ of\ Production\ Hours}$$

Budgeting

The nurse executive and other healthcare leaders must understand the budgeting process and associated outcomes such as cost control, response plan, and market expansion. A *budget* is a plan for coordinating financial goals for an organization. A good budget specifies what needs to be done, by whom, when, and at what cost. *Budgeting* is a formal process characterized as quantitative expression of intentions, plans, and expectations. A budget provides necessary information that allows nurse executives and financial officers to develop actions to control results in future reporting periods. This plan is typically expressed in monetary terms and often lists expectations of a defined entity such as a department, unit, or company.

Developing

Budget development involves collecting information supplied to nurse executives before the annual planning cycle. Three things are provided by budget: the status of each unit or department, and a retrospective history of financial activities, the anticipated revenue for the upcoming year. During the development process, an executive can offer optimistic, moderate, and pessimistic scenarios regarding the budget. During this process, review and approval procedures are completed, and there is an expected timeline to create, revise, and finalize the budget.

Analyzing and Monitoring

Nurse executives are expected to routinely analyze and monitor *budget reports*, usually monthly. Chief financial officers often ask the manager to make adjustments based on deviations from the budget or to justify those deviations. Nurse executives must be familiar with these trends and with trending methodology used in the organization. Over- or under-correction of variance can occur when trends are not considered, leading to difficulties in the future months.

Reporting

Nurse executives usually manage their units or departments with the aid of monthly, quarterly, annual, and predictive *budget reports*. Reports should be assessed for accuracy and checked for hidden content. Today, almost all budget reports are sent electronically.

Justifying

The reason for an expenditure must be known, understood, and justified. Budget items should be consistent with the overall objectives and fiscal plan of the organization. Most facilities have a standard *justification process*, where a nurse executive is requested to justify an expenditure by submitting a business case. The organization will prioritize requests based on set criteria. In special circumstances, long-term benefits can justify budget items that normally result in a negative variance.

Capital Budget

The *capital budget* involves renovation and equipment expenses necessary to attain long-term goals. Typically, they must have a lengthy lifespan that is more than one year and meet a set dollar value. Criteria is defined by organizations for items included in this type of budget. When considering capital items in the budget, the overall cost including actual product cost, delivery charges, installation, and service contracts must be considered.

Part of the capital budgeting process is *amortization*, an assignment of costs to a capital item for its lifetime. Critically important aspects of the "life expectancy" of an item such as a piece of equipment or computer program allow room for development of a replacement strategy. Capital planning can also plan for and predict the various environmental requirements, such as space and buildings, required for a healthcare facility to conduct business.

Operating Budget

The *operating budget* is based on projected expenses and revenues for the *fiscal year*, which is 12 months that do not always occur in the order of the calendar year. It is also referred to as an annual budget. With the operating budget, there is a separation of expense and revenue segments, allowing a simple loss or profit calculation. Management practices are known to significantly impact the operating budget.

Cost-Containment Strategies

Risk Management

Risk management is significant in the healthcare arena, especially with commitments and mandates related to disclosure of adverse events. This service is organization-wide and identifies a problem and takes corrective action to reduce the risk to the facility, personnel, and patients. Risk management is a problem-focused approach to reducing the frequency and severity of injuries, accidents, and adverse events.

The main components of a risk management program include:

- Review of monitoring systems regarding integrity including questionnaires, incident reports, meeting minutes of various committees, audits, and oral complaints
- Identification of actual or potential hazards and inspection to locate problem areas
- Analysis and categorization of incidents and events that result in actual or potential adverse outcomes
- Elimination of risk when identified
- Review and tracking of laws and rules related to legal codes, patient care, and patient safety
- Preparation of reports to keep executives informed of risk management findings and appropriate actions

Reduction in Staff and Services

Reduction in force (RIF) strategies and eliminating services that are not critical to the facility's goals can contain costs. *Outsourcing* is one approach to cost containment. The nurse executive takes vendor proposals for services, such as laundry, housekeeping, and food services. Other services that can be outsourced include payroll, transcription, and data processing. When necessary, temporary agencies can supply core staff to satisfy seasonal requirements. When RIFs achieve cost savings, hidden costs could outweigh anticipated savings, making them unsustainable.

HEALTH AND PUBLIC POLICY

According to the World Health Organization (WHO), health and public policy involves decisions, plans, and actions undertaken by government, state, or local agencies to achieve a specific healthcare goal within a society. This is done to define a vision for the future, outline priorities, inform people, and build consensus. Concepts and elements of health and public policy include mandatory reporting, issues related to health and public policy, legal issues, and consumer-driven healthcare.

Mandatory Reporting

Neglect and Abuse

As of 2012, approximately 48 states and the District of Columbia designate professions whose members are mandated by law to notify authorities of child and elder mistreatment. The individuals designated as mandatory reporters generally have frequent contact with children and/or elderly persons. These people include:

- Social workers
- Physicians, nurses, and other healthcare workers
- Medical examiners and coroners
- Teachers, principals, and other school personnel
- Childcare providers and daycare workers
- Counselors, therapists, and other mental health professionals
- Law enforcement officers

Communicable Disease

Under the regulations to control *communicable diseases* (42 USC 264), when judgment is needed to prevent the introduction and transmission of communicable disease from foreign countries into the U.S. or across state lines, the Surgeon General is authorized to make and enforce regulations. The Surgeon General may inspect, fumigate, disinfect, sanitize, exterminate, and destroy any contaminated and/or infected articles or animals found to be dangerous to humans. This law covers:

- Apprehension, detention, or conditional release of individuals
- Application of regulations to persons from foreign countries entering the U.S.
- Apprehension and examination of persons reasonably believed to be infected
- Pre-exemption

Communicable disease reporting is also called *public health disease surveillance*, which is the ongoing, systematic accumulation, evaluation, and understanding of data regarding disease case occurring in the population. In the U.S., all states have statutes, regulations, and laws that require reporting of infectious and communicable disease. They are also authorized to monitor and collect disease case data in a central repository that detects patterns, outbreaks, and clusters. The catalogue of reportable diseases varies across states, but the criteria that defines a communicable disease are standardized by the Centers for Disease Control and Prevention (CDC) in accord with the Council of State and Territorial Epidemiologists.

All school administrators, childcare facility operators, medical personnel, restaurant owners, and physicians must report suspected or actual communicable diseases to their local health department. Reportable diseases are monitored through the National Healthcare Safety Network (NHSN).

Malpractice and Negligence

Nurses and physicians are often sometimes as defendants in medical *malpractice* lawsuits. According to the National Practitioner Data Bank (NPDB), from 1998 to 2001, the number of malpractice payments made by nurses increased from 253 to 413. The NPDB also reports that the median medical malpractice ward in 2006 was $175,000. This trend continues despite the efforts of nursing educators and managers to inform nurses of their professional responsibilities and limitations. A nurse can be charged with *negligence* as a consequence of any action or inaction that results in patient harm or injury.

When Americans for Insurance Reform (AIR) analyzed insurance industry expenses, they found that during the last decade, while doctors' premiums skyrocketed, inflation-adjusted payouts per doctor did not follow suit and have been stable or falling. Patients are injured by preventable medical errors. The idea that serious medical errors must be reported and made public is widely-held by the public, but states continue to underreport.

The nurse executive becomes involved in negligence when he/she is approached by a nurse, patient, family member, or other person with a complaint. The nurse manager is responsible for the actions of the nurses, so he/she is duty-bound to pass this information on to superiors. The legal and ethical duty of the supervisor is to investigate and intervene when there is an incident or potential danger to patient safety and health.

Health and Public Policy Issues

Healthcare policy is formed mostly through government agencies, in particular the U.S. Department of Health and Human Services nationally and related departments at the state level. One recent concern in health policy is healthcare reform. To make a difference in the outcome of health policies, nurse executives must embrace health policy at the grassroots level.

Healthy People 2020

Healthy People is a program that helps to improve the health of Americans by offering science-based, 10-year national objectives. Healthy People creates benchmarks and monitors progress to measure the impact of preventive activities, to encourage collaboration across sectors and communities, and to empower people to make informed health decisions. Healthy People 2020 reflects input from a diverse group of individuals and organizations and has been an agenda for improving the nation's health for over 10 years. Objectives include increased public awareness of the determinants of health, disability, and disease; provision of local, state, and national objectives and goals; and identification of critical research, data collection, and evaluation needs.

Health Disparities

Health disparities are preventable differences in the burden of injury, violence, and disease and are variances in the opportunities to achieve optimum health and wellness that are experienced by disadvantaged groups or populations. Populations are defined by race, ethnicity, gender, income, disability, geographic location, education, or sexual orientation. Health disparities are inequities that are directly associated with current and historical unequal distribution of political, social, economic, and environmental resources.

Causes of Health Disparities

The causes of health disparities include:
- Poverty
- Inadequate access to healthcare
- Lack of education
- Individual and behavioral factors
- Environmental threats

Health Disparities Report

In a recent report by the Agency for Healthcare Research and Quality (2013c), numerous health disparities were found. These include:
- Hispanics, Blacks, American Indians, Asians, and Native Alaskans received worse care than Whites
- Poor or low-income individuals did not receive the same level of health care of high-income individuals
- Blacks, Asians, Hispanics, Native Americans, and Native Alaskans all had worse access to care than Whites

- High-income people had better access to care than poor people
- In 2005, Americans did not receive 1/3 of the healthcare services needed
- In 2002, 24% Americans reported difficulties accessing healthcare, and by 2009, 26% encountered these difficulties

Healthcare Reform Initiatives

In 2010, President Obama introduced what would eventually be the Health Care and Education Reconciliation Act Patient Protection and Affordable Care Act which was amended to. This legislation is controversial, with many states challenging it in federal court. The U.S. Supreme Court found the law to be constitutional in 2012 in a 5 to 4 decision. This act affects the availability and terms of healthcare insurance, includes the expansion of Medicaid, and will become effective January 1, 2014.

The Affordable Care Act called for the creation of the Patient-Centered Outcomes Research Institute, which studies comparative effectiveness research that is funded by a fee on those insured. It also allows the FDA to approve generic drugs, with 12 years of exclusive use for new biologic medications. Additionally, this law involves programs that increase incentives to provide collaborative and quality healthcare.

Legal Issues

Healthcare Fraud and Abuse

Healthcare fraud is when a person or group obtains some unauthorized benefit through intentional misrepresentation or deception. *Abuse* in healthcare is when provider practices are not consistent with medical or business practices, resulting in unnecessary costs or reimbursements that do not meet healthcare standards or are not medically necessary.

Whistleblowing

The Whistleblower Protection Act of 1989 protects government employees who report misconduct by an organization or agency. Whistleblowers can report a violation of: a law, regulation, or rule; gross waste of funds; gross mismanagement; a substantial, specific danger to public safety and health; or an abuse of authority.

Whistleblower complaints at the federal level are investigated by the Office of Special Counsel. These complaints are then adjudicated by the judicial agency, the Merit

Systems Protection Board. The only court of appeals that hears appeals of whistleblower cases is The Federal Circuit.

Health Insurance Portability and Accountability Act (HIPAA)

The Health Insurance Portability and Accountability Act (HIPAA) of 1996 involves the electronic exchange and protection of healthcare information and patient data. This law allows persons who change an employment relationship to immediately qualify for health insurance coverage. Also, the law authorizes U.S. Department of Health and Human Services to require the use of healthcare data exchange, transmission, and protection criteria. Healthcare organizations and systems must comply with this law.

Corporate Compliance

Corporate compliance initiatives include waste, fraud, and abuse, and they are significant in the business area of healthcare. Healthcare facilities are required to have in place corporate compliance systems designed to prevent regulatory and legal violations, to establish principles that demonstrate the organization's commitment to a high standard of business practice, and to identify fraud and abuse within the healthcare system.

Harassment

Lateral violence is a form of harassment common to the field of nursing. In this case, nurses show aggressive or destructive behavior against each other or one group against a person or group. The end result is damage to someone's confidence, self-esteem, or dignity. Lateral violence can consist of intentional and unintentional acts meant to intimidate, harm, or humiliate a person or group of people. This form of *harassment* puts patients and other workers at risk for poor outcomes. Nurse executives can address lateral violence in the workplace and implement strategies to prevent and/or eliminate this behavior. These strategies include:

- Disciplining any staff member or manager who engages in this behavior
- Educating the staff and managers about lateral violence
- Having an open culture or transparency
- Creating a culture intolerant to harassment

Negligence and Malpractice

Nurses often confuse the terms negligence and malpractice, assuming they are synonymous. *Negligence* is the failure to do what is reasonable and necessary (omission) or doing something that others would not do under the circumstances (commission). *Malpractice* goes beyond negligence; the four main elements that constitute malpractice are:

- Duty – How would a prudent and reasonable provider behave in this situation?

- Breach of Duty – Did the provider breach the standard of care in this circumstance?

- Causation – Was the provider's inappropriate, unreasonable, or careless behavior the cause of insult or injury?

- Injury – Did the patient suffer insult or injury?

Consumer-Driven Healthcare

Public Reporting

Public reporting is publicly available data that is free of charge or at a low cost that concerns healthcare process, organization, or outcome at any provider level (individual, clinician, group, or organization) or at the health plan level. In 2012, researchers for the Agency for Healthcare Research and Quality (AHRQ) conducted a comprehensive literature review and found public reporting has a marked association with higher healthcare performance measures. Additional findings included:

- Publicly reported quality measures actually showed improvement over time.
- When data is made public, providers appear to pursue strategies to improve quality.
- No evidence supports the idea that patients and their families are affected by public reporting when selecting a healthcare provider.

Hospital Consumer Assessment of Healthcare Providers and Systems (HCAHPS)

The CMS partnered with the AHRQ to develop HCAHPS. These two Department of Health and Human Service organizations developed an initiative to measure patient perspectives on hospital care through the use of a standardized data collection methods and surveys. Hospitals can combine the survey's core questions with a customized set that complement each hospital's information for improving activities related to quality and internal customer services.

Chapter 2: Exemplary Professional Practice

This chapter covers the concepts and elements of exemplary professional practice including care management and healthcare delivery, professional practice environment and models, communication, and quality care monitoring and improvement.

CARE MANAGEMENT AND HEALTHCARE DELIVERY

Healthcare Delivery Models

The Internet and Telehealth

The Internet provides instant, available information and the ability for a healthcare worker or nurse executive to connect with colleagues and resources in other states and countries. *Telehealth* (also called telemedicine or ehealth) is the use of computer technology and small video cameras to allow healthcare professionals to provide necessary services. A video recording can be transmitted immediately to healthcare providers so that patient assessment and intervention can begin immediately. Not restrained by distance or time, this transmission allows patients in remote locations to enjoy the same level of consultation as people who live near medical facilities.

Network Systems

Networks allow entities to communicate and provide a service to the community. They also are a means to consolidate power, a mode for market sharing, and a way to enhance fiscal solvency through collective purchasing power. In a *decentralized system*, direct communication occurs in all directions and without restriction. With a *centralized system*, communication requires that input and output be controlled through a central point. Finally, a *restricted system* places international barriers between organizations and groups.

Management Information Systems

A Management Information System (MIS) has value to the business of healthcare. These systems are necessary to document clinical findings and care, conduct business, capture trends, and meet the daily demands of healthcare delivery. A *local area network* (LAN) is several personal computers linked together through a server. This system allows for communication among organization personnel. A *wide area network* (WAN) is a system that consists of many LANs where connections are affected by specialized networking software.

Electronic Data Transfer

Electronic data transfer improves healthcare integration. The electronic health record is now a universal reality. The several levels of products that provide electronic patient information transfer include:

- Automated Medical Record (AMR) – Considered a first-level product, the AMR brings together data from other sources and delivers it electronically to the user.

- Computerized Medical Record System (CMRS) – With this product, paper-based items are now available electronically via scanning.

- Electronic Medical Record (EMR) – This third-level product delivers capability for electronic information and data entry, data integrity, auditing, and electronic signature.

- Electronic Patient Record (EPR) – This product brings together patient information from more than one organization or healthcare facility.

- Electronic Health Record (EHR) – This fifth-level product provides the user with patient information, including data not pertaining to his/her medical problem or health condition, from multiple sources.

Laws, Regulations, and Accreditation

Registration

The main responsibility of the state boards of nursing is to protect the public. These boards control the nursing licensure process and "register" nurses to practice under the rules and regulations of their specific governing body; this is known as *registration*. State boards must protect the public from unlawful or unscrupulous practice by licensed nurses. Licenses can be sanctioned, suspended, or revoked for those who violate a law or who are convicted of specified crimes.

Licensure

Licensure is the process of granting permission to a person to practice in a given profession. The licensure's purpose is to protect against unlicensed or untrained persons. Licensure for nursing is regulated by each state through the National Council of State Boards of Nursing, which oversees the National Council Licensure Examination for Practical Nurses (NCLEX-PN) and the National Council Licensure Examination for

Registered Nurses (NCLEX-RN) tests. These tests demonstrate that the candidate meets the qualifications required to practice within the specified scope. All states now grant reciprocity to nurses who move from one state to another if they apply for and receive a license to practice in the second state.

Nurse compact legislation allows a licensed nurse to practice in states where they did not obtain their license without having to apply for a second license. This growing trend is endorsed in most states, and model legislative language exists for licensure recognition. The *nurse compact* implies that state agencies must surrender certain measures of parochial control of practice within their regions.

Certification
Certification recognizes nurses who meet certain requirements, generally for a particular field or clinical specialty, but does not include a legal scope of nursing practice. Certification is not mandatory, but many state boards of nursing use professional certification for a stipulation for advanced practice nurses (APNs). Certification is a hallmark of excellence in specialty practice.

The Joint Commission
The Joint Commission is the best known of all U.S. accrediting bodies. The Joint Commission on the Accreditation of Hospitals (JCAH), established in 1951, sets the standards for and accredits approximately 16,000 healthcare facilities in the U.S. In addition to acute care hospitals, the Joint Commission also accredits critical access facilities, medical equipment services, home healthcare and hospice agencies, rehabilitation centers, physician practices, surgical centers, skilled nursing homes, and independent laboratories.

The Joint Comission provides Disease-Specific Care Certification to hospitals and other health-related organizations. They also have a Health Care Staffing Services Certification program. To improve the Americans' quality of healthcare, the Joint Commission partners with and consults government agencies and Congress. The standards this group sets forth address a healthcare organization's performance level in infection control, patient treatment, and patient rights. In 2009, the Joint Commission Internet *E-dition* became available. This web-based tool provides all standards and requirements for Joint Commission accreditation.

National Committee for Quality Assurance (NCQA)

The National Committee for Quality Assurance (NCQA) deals with quality measures that show the degree of improvement in nursing practice and focus on evidence-based interventions. In 2002, the NCQA reported that if agencies adopted best practices, more than 22 million sick days could be avoided and 6,000 lives could be saved.

The NCQA Health Plan Employer Data and Information Set (HEDIS) system measures the comparative quality of healthcare systems and plans. Used by employer groups and benefits managers, this system gives recommendations to employees about different health plans during open enrollment periods.

The National Database of Nursing Quality Indicators (NDNQI) is affiliated with the ANA's Quality and Safety Initiative. With this system, data from more than 250 U.S. hospitals is obtained and used to determine the effect of nursing on patient outcomes.

Centers for Medicare and Medicaid Services

In 2010, the Medicare and Medicaid program formed the Center for Program Integrity (CPI), which gathered oversight of Medicare and Medicaid program integrity to organize best practices and resources to improve programs comprehensively. The Small Business Jobs Act and the Affordable Care Act are two forms of legislation to provide additional opportunities to combat abuse, fraud, and waste.

Medicare

The Medicare program, established in 1965, paid for healthcare services for individuals older than 64. This act was initially aimed at the retirement age population, but after an expansion in 1972 now includes end stage renal disease patients and others whose disabilities meet Medicare's definition. Currently, 90% of Medicare beneficiaries are 65 years of age or older.

Medicaid

The Medicaid program, a welfare program, was established in 1965 to pay for specific required health services for low-income children and their parents or guardians. These funds are administered through the Temporary Assistance for Needy Families (TANF) program. The Medicaid program has expanded to include coverage for people with developmental disabilities and other low-income groups such as children, pregnant women, and the elderly.

Models of Nursing Practice

Governance Models
Unit-level governance can take a variety of forms. In the *traditional hierarchy*, the nurse executive supervises nurse managers who supervise charge nurses who supervise staff nurses. The *shared governance model* allows staff nurses to be part of the decision-making process about the healthcare facility or their unit of service. This empowers frontline healthcare providers to actively participate with policy making and decisions within the organization.

Clinical Pathways
Clinical pathways define intended outcomes, provide direction for healthcare, and allow multidisciplinary teams to collaborate and communicate. Also known as *critical paths*, *clinical practice guidelines*, and *clinical protocols*, these pathways are evidence-based and follow the law of averages. The extent to which clinical pathways form the basis of practice has not yet been determined.

Clinical Advancement Programs
Clinical advancement programs (also called *career ladders* or *clinical ladders*) foster recognition of professional and expert nurses and offer a career pathway that will allow them to continue providing direct care for patients. Those who choose to pursue clinical advancement must demonstrate expertise through references from colleagues and supervisors. Also, the nurse must show how his/her application of the nursing process has impacted the outcome of patient care.

Using Population Served to Create Workflow

Patient-Centered Medical Home (PCMH)
The AHRQ formed the Patient-Centered Medical Home (PCMH) as a representative for transforming healthcare organizations and supplying of primary care. This model transforms the way that primary care is delivered and organized and helps improve healthcare in the U.S. The PCMH's five functions and attributes are:
- Comprehensive Care – PCMH's objective is to meet the majority of patients' physical and mental healthcare requirements such as chronic and acute care, wellness, and prevention. Comprehensive care involves a team of health providers such as social workers, nurses, pharmacists, physicians, and nutritionists.

- Patient-Centered – Primary care that is relationship-based with a holistic approach is provided by the PCMH model. This involves considering the entire family with respect to patient needs, culture, values, and preferences.

- Coordinated Care – Care is coordinated across all aspects of the healthcare system such as hospitals, community services, specialty care, and home health. This coordination helps to smooth transitions between sites of care.

- Accessible Services – The PCMH model delivers accessible healthcare and services with shorter wait times for patient needs, 24/7 electronic or telephone access to healthcare providers, and enhanced in-person hours.

- Quality and Safety – A commitment to quality improvement is demonstrated by this model through enduring activities including evidence-based nursing, medicine, and clinical decision-support tools that guide decision making.

Case Management

A growing field in the nursing profession is *case management*. An RN or APN is placed in the position of managing the total care of a group of patients as they move through the continuum of care. Case managers coordinate necessary care for patients based on certain characteristics of the group. Most case managers have a responsibility to review the relative effectiveness and cost of proposed or given care and for approving or denying any requested interventions.

Interdisciplinary Team

Healthcare providers from many professions who have the same common patient care goals and common patient population make up an *interdisciplinary team*. These professionals are actively interdependent and continually communicate to assure the integration of various aspects of healthcare needs. The interdisciplinary team is different from the *multidisciplinary care* approach and the *consultative approach*. The main professionals of the interdisciplinary team include: physicians, nurses (various levels), physician assistants, pharmacists, social workers, psychologists, occupational and physical therapists, language and speech pathologists, dietitians, and dentists.

PROFESSIONAL PRACTICE ENVIRONMENT AND MODELS

According to Hoffart and Woods (1996), a *professional practice model* (PPM) is a system (process, structure, or value) that supports registered nurse control over the delivery of nursing care and the healthcare environment. The five subsystems of PPM include: compensation and rewards, management approach, patient care delivery model, professional relationships, and values. The two most commonly used healthcare delivery systems are primary nursing and case management.

Professional Practice Models

Case Method Nursing
The case method of delivering nursing care is often called *total patient care*. All aspects of patient care are an RN's responsibility. The *case method nursing* care approach is often practiced in intensive care settings or in home healthcare settings. In addition to the nursing process, the RN is responsible for all indirect and direct patient care functions, and he/she communicates needs, changes, and request for assistance to a charge nurse or team leader. The case method is considered to be holistic because it provides comprehensive care. Disadvantages of this system are the lack of continuity between shifts, the cost of RNs, and the need for an adequate supply of RNs.

Functional Nursing
The *functional nursing* care delivery system is a task-oriented method in which individual caregivers are not assigned to patients. Instead, each nurse performs specific assigned tasks for all patients in a given unit or area. The task of medication administration is often assigned to an RN, whereas LPNs deliver more of the hands-on care, and nursing assistants complete basic hygiene tasks. In a functional model, the RN in charge must coordinate the care of all patients.

Team Nursing
Team nursing is a method developed in the 1950s in response to complaints regarding functional nursing. With this approach, patients are assigned to a team of nurses, therapists, dietitians, and assistants. The typical unit of 30 patients will have a charge nurse, two or three team leaders, and two or three additional team members per each of the teams. The team leader assigns all patients to the members of the team and delegates tasks according to members' skills and competence.

Primary Nursing

Developed in the late 1960s, *primary nursing* is a patient care system where a primary nurse is responsible for planning patient care and delegating tasks when he/she is not present. The nurse is responsible for 24-hour care delivery. The nurse who assists the primary nurse during off-duty hours is considered to be an associate nurse, and this person follows the set plan of care. Nurse practitioners, clinical nurse specialists, and physician extenders often function within this system as consultants to the primary nurse.

Role Delineation

Credentialing

Credentialing describes the program designation processes when institutions or individuals meet an organization's established standards. The standards can be mandatory and minimum or can be voluntary and above minimum. Part of the credentialing process involves licensure, accreditation, registration, certification, recognition, and/or endorsement.

The stamps or marks of achievement and quality are called *credentials*, and they communicate to consumers, employers, employees, and payers the expectation of a credentialed person, program, facility, product, equipment, device, or service. Credentials may be periodically renewed to assure the public and interested parties of continued quality. Credentials can also be removed when the behavior or competence standards are unmet, maintained, or continued.

Certification

In the process of *certification* a non-governmental organization, association, or agency verifies that an individual is qualified to practice a profession and has met the standards necessary for specialty practice. Certification assures the public and concerned parties that a professional has mastered the skills and knowledge of a certain area.

When a non-governmental entity recognizes and credentials a person after they have met standardized, established criteria, this voluntary process is called professional certification. This allows a profession to differentiate its members by using standards, which are based on existing requirements, criteria, and legal regulations.

Recognition

Recognition is the process where an association, organization, or agency accepts the credentialing status of another credentialing body for specified purposes.

Professional Practice Standards

There are various *professional practice standards* including the ANA Scope and Standards, the Code of Ethics for Nurses, the ANA Bill of Rights for Registered Nurses, and the U.S. Nurse Practice Acts. A standard is an authoritative statement enunciated and promulgated by a profession, and it is a set criteria that judges the quality of education, service, and practice is judged. These statements describe the roles and responsibilities for which healthcare providers are accountable, and they reflect the priorities and values of the profession. Nursing standards set outcomes that are a nurse's responsibility, establish the accountability of profession to the public, and frame nursing practice's evaluation, and provide direction for professional nursing practice.

ANA Scope and Standards

Nurses are accountable to the public for aspects of practice. The ANA has developed standards for nursing practice and the scope of practice. Standards of practice describe the common performance and level of care by which the quality of practice is to be determined and the responsibilities for which nurses are accountable. The two elements of the nursing practice standards are the professional performance standards and nursing care standards.

The *standards of nursing care* are guidelines for practice, which are general to any specialty or setting. They follow the nursing process's broad categories of evaluation, implementation, , planning, outcome identification, diagnosis, and assessment. The *standards of professional performance* address the nursing role with regard to ethics, research, education, collegiality, and resource utilization (Robinson, 2010).

Code of Ethics for Nurses

A *code of ethics* is a formal statement by an association, organization, or agency that expresses that entity's values and ideals. This set of ethical principles has been agreed on by members of that entity, and they reflect moral judgments, serve as a standard for professional actions, and define expectations (Osborn, Wraa, & Watson, 2010).

The purpose of the nursing code of ethics is to:

- Provide a sign of the profession's commitment to excellence in public service
- Inform the public of the minimum standards of the nursing profession
- Help the public understand the nursing code of conduct
- Outline the main ethical considerations of this profession
- Guide nurses in self-regulation
- Provide ethical standards for professional behavior

ANA Bill of Rights for RNs

Registered nurses alleviate the suffering of patients, families, groups, and communities while providing services that maintain respect for patient individuality and human dignity. They restore, maintain, and promote health; shelter patients in their care; and prevent illness. To defend nurse's autonomy and dignity in the healthcare workplace, the ANA's Bill of Rights for professional nurses gives them the right to:

- Practice in a manner that fulfills their obligations to society and to those who receive nursing care
- Practice in environments that allow them to act in accordance with professional standards and legally authorized scopes of practice
- A work environment that supports and facilitates ethical practice in accordance with the *Code of Ethics for Nurses with Interpretive Statements*
- Freely and openly advocate for themselves and their patients without fear of retribution
- Fair compensation for their work, consistent with their knowledge, experience, and professional responsibilities
- A work environment that is safe for themselves and their patients.
- Negotiate the conditions of their employment, either as individuals or collectively, in all practice settings[7]

U.S. Nurse Practice Acts

The practice of nursing requires independent decision making, specialized skills, and certain knowledge. Nursing practice varies according to the type of patient, setting, disease state, therapeutic approaches, and level of rehabilitation. The U.S. Nurse Practice Acts are legislations that guide and govern nursing practice. Every state has enacted a nurse practice act (NPA) that is enforced by its legislature. Rules and

---

[7] "Nurse's Bill of Rights," American Nurses Association, accessed November 5, 2015, http://www.nursingworld.org/NursesBillofRights.

regulations are consistent with these acts and must endure a public review process before being enacted. After being ratified, these regulations have the full effect of law.

The specificity of NPAs varies from state to state. However, all NPAs include:
- Education program standards
- Authority and power of a board of nursing
- Standards of nursing practice
- Licensure requirements
- Grounds for disciplinary action
- Types of licenses and titles

Developing Clinical Staff

Team Building
A team is developed for the purpose of some sort of work. In nursing, the team of professionals remains the most powerful unit of performance within an organization. Some communication skills necessary for nurse executives to build team cohesiveness include the ability to express one's ideas decisively and clearly and the ability to listen and invite opinions. A team's success depends on members' work behaviors. The team leader serves as a facilitator for the *team-building* process and team activities.

Group Dynamics
Group development has four predictable stages. The *forming* stage is where a cluster is formed from individuals coming together. The second stage is known as the *storming* stage where the group proceeds through the maturation process and determines a leader. During the third stage, called *norming*, the rules of working as a group are clarified and relationships and roles are made explicit. In the final stage, called *performing*, the group does most of the work and focuses energies on achieving goals.

Orientation
Orientation defines role expectations and introduces new members of the staff to the facility's policies, knowledge, culture, and skills they need to perform safely and independently in a healthcare environment. Orientation typically begins when the member accepts terms of employment and agrees to the job requirements. The length of orientation programs for temporary staff can be as short as 3 days, while long-term employees can be in orientation anywhere from 4 to 12 weeks. This time frame is set by the organization and should be clearly communicated to the employee.

Most orientation programs have two phases: a general facility orientation and the unit-specific orientation. The *general facility orientation* involves introduction and education concerning the entire healthcare facility, whereas the *unit-specific orientation* focuses on the actual worksite of the new employee. The Joint Commission's standard HR.01.04.01 mandates relevant hospital-wide and unit-specific orientations programs with procedure and policy focuses. The orientation's completion must be recorded.

Most orientations incorporate safety discussions, a facility's organizational structure and mission, patient privacy issues and standards (HIPAA), payroll and benefit issues, and regulatory requirements. Others topics that might comprise a staff competency checklist are offered by the Joint Commission, including educational requirements, training, evaluation, competency, and orientation. These are located at: http://www.jointcommission.org/standards/SII/.

Competency Validation

Assessment and documentation of staff *competency* is mandated by the Joint Commission (HR.01.06.01, 2009). Many worksites initially use a checklist to complete *competency validation*. Included on the checklists are the area's equipment and procedures and a rating system that the new employees can use to measure their encounter with the items. Because every person's abilities and perception varies, these checklists are not completely precise. One competency validation tool is the Performance-Based Development System (PBDS). This system focuses on the tool's critical-thinking and interpersonal components. It also is an excellent way to assess critical-thinking skills and the person's reflection on what was learned (Byrne, 2009).

Preceptors

Experienced staff members who help with new employee orientation are called *preceptors*. This person is responsible for making the new employee feel comfortable within the team. A few preceptor programs offer compensation for this service. Most organizations make precepting a requirement for advancement on a clinical ladder. Preceptors must understand adult learning principles that are used by nurse educators to develop educational activities.

Professional Healthcare Environment

Cultural Competence

Cultural competence is the capability to cooperate with people of varying cultures and ethnicities, while being personally aware of one's attitude toward culture. A nurse executive will manage nurses of varying cultures and patients of many ethnicities and races. In today's globalized world, cultural competence is a vital management strategy. The world population is expected to double by the year 2050, and developing nations will account for 80% of the growth. A culturally competent leader can manage individual expectations, provide clear decision-making strategies, and allow employees the opportunity to grow.

Strategies for cultural competence include:
- Knowing and understanding your own values, biases, and culture
- Emphasizing corporate values
- Considering the rules and procedures from all perspectives
- Giving straightforward instructions and using adequate resources
- Demonstrating personal cultural awareness

Critical Thinking

Nursing is a challenging profession that is associated with a rapidly changing healthcare environment. The essence of nursing involves the decision-making process and a professional's willingness to act on those decisions. A nurse must have the ability to think critically and use sound clinical judgment. *Critical thinking* is not a class that is taught nor is it a body of knowledge that is learned. Critical thinking can occur in all areas of life and learning; it is defined as a purposeful, goal-directed, and self-regulatory process that is context bound.

Critical-thinking skills are necessary for observing, gathering, organizing, and analyzing data. When applied to patient care situations, critical thinking promotes health and assists with desired outcomes. The five essential elements of the critical-thinking process are:
- Information collection
- Situation analysis
- Generation of alternatives
- Selection of alternatives
- Evaluation

It is important that nursing leaders create an environment where critical thinking is nurtured and encouraged. This involves independent, individual, and divergent thinking skills that are necessary to avoid group thinking and the pressure of conforming to one person's idea. The experience of both negative and positive outcomes can promote critical thinking.

Leveraging Diversity

When a facility achieves cultural competence and values diversity, at a corporate and individual level, the facility is said to be *leveraging diversity*. This business strategy connects the marketplace, the workforce, and the workplace structure. Leveraging diversity can work to improve problem-solving abilities, decision-making skills, and employee morale and reduce grievances. This management approach enables all employees to understand, value, and utilize their skills in order to benefit the facility.

Leveraging diversity entails three elements of leadership behavioral:

- Leadership element – This involves providing a feeling of purpose, meaning, and direction to employees that offers them with the opportunity to recognize their full potential.

- Cultural element – This involves influencing the tone of an organization's culture with principles, values, or beliefs.

- Connectivity element – This involves connecting cultural and leadership elements with certain aspects of the organization such as vision clarity, power sharing, and intellectual capital.

Organization Transparency

Organizational transparency is the deliberate move away from opaqueness to establish stakeholders' trust. This is a condition where leadership fosters access to participation, decision making, and information. This concept implies a trusting environment, which requires consensus and clarity about what constitutes success. However, the transparency of an organization cannot ensure that the right things will be done. Nurse executives support the mission of an organization by being role models, participating in decision making for the organization, and promoting communication between management and employees and vice versa.

Emotional Intelligence

Emotional intelligence (EI) describes the procedures involved in understanding, identifying, controlling, and utilizing emotional states to regulate behavior and solve problems. This involves one's own and others' emotions. Nurse executives are in the position to recognize what is affecting employees. Good leadership involves understanding emotional intelligence. A framework for emotional intelligence is provided by the Ability-Based Model. Its four elements include:

- Understanding emotions – This is the aptitude to understand emotional language.

- Using emotions – This is the capability to promote cognitive activities with the use of emotions.

- Perceiving emotions – This is the aptitude to identify emotions in voices, faces, and cultural artifacts and the ability to identify one's own emotional state.

- Managing emotions – This is the capability to direct your own and others' emotions.

Resolving Conflict within the Practice Environment

Conflict happens within and between individuals and groups occasionally or often (depending on the personalities). The five types of conflict that can occur in the practice environment are:

- Intrapersonal – The conflict is within you.

- Interpersonal – The conflict is between you and another person.

- Intergroup – The conflict is between members in two or more groups.

- Intragroup – The conflict is between members within a group.

- Competitive – The desired outcome is to overcome your opponent.

A significant part of a nurse executive's time is spend resolving conflicts. Experts have estimated that at least 1/4 of time is spent on conflict management. The goal of *conflict resolution* is to help the interested parties reach a "win-win" outcome where both parties feel resolved. Common approaches for this are:

- Appealing to the requests of both individuals or parties
- Emphasizing goals and deemphasizing personalities
- Building consensus

COMMUNICATION

The care of patients involves many different individuals and all types of healthcare providers. Therefore, it is necessary for there to be effective and meaningful *communication* for healthcare delivery. Communication systems are formal and informal structures used to support the communication needs within an organization. Elements of these systems are the communication channel, type of message, policies, agent, services, device, interaction mode, and security protocol. Also, effective communication relies on useful style and principles of information sharing, negotiation concepts and strategies, and communication processes that support safe patient care.

Communication Systems

Communication systems are structures used by a healthcare facility to support the exchange of information. They can be either formal or informal, involve people or groups, and use technology or other modes of transfer. The elements of a communication system include:

- Communication channel – This is the "pipeline" along which a message must travel that runs from the initiator to the recipient. These include telephone, email, reports, staff meetings, board meetings, presentation, one-on-one conversation, consumer feedback, and patient/family council.

- Type of message – Messages can be structured (formal) or unstructured (informal). When messages are sent via an email or telephone recording, they will usually be in a standard format.

- Policies – Communication policies are used to shape communication system performance, which is independent from the technologies used.

- Agent – The agent is the person responsible for transmitting information from one person to another or from one person to a group.

- Services – There are numerous computer software applications for providing communication services. These include fax, voicemail, and text messages.

- Device – Examples of communication devices include fax machines, telephones, and personal digital assistants (PDAs).

- Interaction mode – The way the interaction is designed relies on the information system. Some modes of interaction, such as the ring of a telephone, require that the recipient of the message pay attention.

- Security protocol – In the healthcare environment, patient privacy concerns make it important that unintended recipients do not gain access to clinical records or patient information. The facility will use a security protocol to reflect the degree of risk associated with the content of the message.

Principles of Communication

Communication principles include:

- Active listening – This communication technique requires that the listener repeat back to the speaker what he/she hears to confirm understanding between both parties.

- Reflective – This communication strategy helps to comprehend the speaker's thoughts, then offers said thought back to the speaker in an attempt to reconstruct it and relay understanding.

- Two-way – This communication technique is a form of transmission in which both parties transmit information. This technique includes chat rooms, instant messaging, telephone conversations, and in-person discussions.

- Interviewing – This communication technique is a conversation between two or more people. This is done in medial reporting, in qualitative research, in employee statements, and to retrieve facts.

Communication Styles

Five well-known *communication styles* are:

- Persuasive – This style encourages others to view ideas as beneficial to their needs, displays authority to build trust, and reassures staff by creating an emotive and empathetic connection.

- Assertive – This style involves standing up for personal rights and expressing feelings, beliefs, and thoughts in an honest, direct, and appropriate way that does not violate another individual's rights.

- Passive – This style involves violating your own rights by failing to express your feelings, beliefs, and thoughts and by allowing others to violate your rights. This is often done in a timid, apologetic manner.

- Aggressive – This style involves violating the rights of others by directly standing up for your personal rights in an inappropriate manner.

- Passive-aggressive – This style involves expressing your feelings, beliefs, and thoughts in a confusing and unclear way.

Negotiation Concepts and Strategies

Negotiation is a formal process that takes place during the contract deliberations of management and unions. It is also a political process that involves "power play" among competing individuals. The four main principles necessary for successful negotiations are:

- Separation – This involves the separation of the person/people and the problem.

- Focus – This involves focusing on the interests of the patient or healthcare facility, not those of the person/people or a position.

- Invention – This involves creating options for mutual gains.

- Insistence – This involves meeting objective criteria.

With interest-based negotiation, leaders focus on treating people as equals and on resolving issues on their merits rather than on positions or political interest. With this concept, strategies include defining issues with a definition acceptable to both parties, developing options that will meet the needs and interests of all concerned individuals, and applying objective standards to resolve conflict.

Communication Procedures for Maintaining Safe Patient Care

Documentation

Documentation of patient care is important for numerous areas of healthcare. Clear, concise documentation assists with accurate coding for care and treatment for billing and reimbursement purposes, and it promotes continuity of care and ensures compliance with regulations. One form of documentation is the *healthcare directive*. Healthcare directives are legal in all states, but the requirements for their authorization and content vary. An *advanced directive* has two parts: appointment of an agent or surrogate for decisions and specific instruction regarding care and treatment. In the acute care setting, the nurse must ensure that documentation regarding the presence of such a directive is done and that ongoing issues regarding the patient's wishes are addressed.

Handoffs and Handovers

A part of communicating in the interest of safe patient care involves transferring vital info and patient care responsibility from one nurse to another. An effective *handoff* (or handover) includes transitioning crucial details and continuous treatment and care. Other terms for handoff include sign over, sign out, cross-coverage, and shift report. Handoff can be intricate and involves communication during a shift change, transfer of records and tools, and interaction between care providers.

Reporting Sentinel Events

Sentinel events are unexpected occurrences that have the potential to result in or actually cause death or injury. Serious injury specifically involves the loss of function or of a limb. The Joint Commission publishes sentinel event alerts that advise healthcare facilities of system or process failures that have caused errors in the past. Recent alerts are defined by errors or events that threaten patient or staff safety such as fires in surgical areas, prevention of ventilator-related infections, and misadministration of potassium chloride.

Appropriate Communication for the Situation and Audience

Part of communication involves the transfer of information from one person to another or others. Methods for this transfer include one-on-one conversation, email, report, patient/family council, board meeting, staff meeting, presentation, and consumer feedback.

QUALITY CARE MONITORING AND IMPROVEMENT

When continuous and systemic actions result in measurable improvements in patient groups' health statuses and services, this is called *quality improvement* (QI). The level of health services improvement is directly correlated the desired outcomes of patients and/or patient populations. Principles of QI focus on:

- QI work as systems and processes
- Patients
- Teams
- Use of data

Systems Theories

The concept underlying the *systems theory* maintains that systems are composed of interrelated parts and that these parts are arranged to form a unified whole. Systems are either closed or open. *Closed systems*, such as the circulatory system, occur only in physical sciences. *Open systems* interact internally and externally with the environment. A healthcare facility is considered a complex open system. The parts of this system are: input, throughput, and output. *Input* involves staff, patients, financial resources, materials, equipment, and supplies. *Throughput* involves the actions completed to create a product. *Output* is the product within the healthcare system such as health, death, education, and research.

Continuous Performance Improvement

The Plan-Do-Study-Act (PDSA) Cycle

A section of the Institute for Healthcare Improvement model is the Plan-Do-Study-Act (PDSA) cycle, which can be used to accelerate improvement in quality. A healthcare facility establishes a team, develops standards that identify if a change results in improvement, and then tests the effects of those measures in the workplace. The *PDSA cycle* system tests a modification through planning, implementing, observing, and evaluating.

Steps in the PDSA Cycle
1. <u>Plan</u>: Organize the observation or test including data collection.

2. <u>Do</u>: Test the procedure on a small scale.

3. <u>Study</u>: Study the results and analyze the data.

4. <u>Act</u>: Use the knowledge acquired from the study to create a change.

Root Cause Analysis

Root cause analysis (RCA), a structured method, identifies underlying problems that increase the likelihood of errors and analyzes serious adverse events. Now, it widely serves as a tool for error analysis. The goal of RCA is to identify both active and latent (hidden) errors. RCA follows a specified protocol that starts with reconstructing the incident in question and collecting data through record review and participant interviews. A team of people from varying disciplines analyzes the error's preceding sequence of events, detecting why and how it happened. RCA's goal is to eliminate latent errors that result in adverse events, preventing future harm or injury.

Benchmarking

Benchmarking is a technique that identifies top quality as a means of comparing one's practice or healthcare facility with those judged objectively to be the standard of a certain category. Magnet hospital projects highlight institutions that meet or exceed the highest standards of patient care. Internal benchmarks also identify a particular department or unit that has a consistent track record of excellence.

Report Cards

Report cards are issued by accrediting bodies such as payers or the Joint Commission. These agencies ensure that the healthcare facility meets the minimum requirements of predetermined criteria. Report cards compare facilities or organizations with one another or with pre-established industry benchmarks. Institutions that want to excel in the area of quality must use the tools and techniques offered by accrediting agencies such as the Institute for Healthcare Improvement (IHI) and National Institute of Standards and Technology (NIST).

Functional Status

Functional areas within an organization include marketing, human resources, production, distribution, finance, and research and development. Each functional unit must accurately perform its work so the organization can achieve goals and surpass competitors. The *functional status* of an organization involves areas that are interdependent. Failure to achieve intended results in one or more of these functional areas can result in problems in other areas. The representatives of these functional areas must be in constant contact with each other to maintain optimum functional status.

Required Quality Outcome Measures

Performance Improvement

Performance improvement (PI) activities are those that involve the quality structure of most healthcare facilities and medical organizations. The Plan-Do-Check-Act (PDCA) cycle is one model that is used to understand and represent change over time. This cycle gives nurse leaders the common language and tools to engage in the PI process.

Continuous Quality Improvement

The process of *Continuous quality improvement* (CQI) involves continually increasing quality. This process helps healthcare facilities focus on the vital interventions that have the most applicability to health outcomes and to continued accreditation. As a particular goal is met or achieved, improvement must then be sustained so the stakes remain raised. Measurement of CQI continues until techniques, tools, and behavior patterns become part of daily practices for a predetermined period of time (Rundio & Wilson, 2010).

Total Quality Management

The process of *Total quality management* (TQM) entails the commitment of continuous improvement to be instilled in everyone employed by the healthcare facility. The impact of TQM on productivity and quality is well-documented. The Malcolm Baldridge National Quality Award honors businesses that maintain a commitment to TQM, and the ANCC Magnet Recognition Program honors healthcare facilities that demonstrate sustained excellence in nursing care.

Stakeholder Satisfaction

Many *stakeholders'* vested interested is in a healthcare organization. These stakeholders include:

- Patient and Family – According to research, a direct correlation exists between employee satisfaction and patient satisfaction. *Patient satisfaction* surveys are conducted to determine the perception of the services the patient receives. The definition of quality often differs between the patient/family and the healthcare facility. The results of these surveys help organization leaders to create and revise the marketing plan.

- Staff and Physicians – For many healthcare facilities, a high rate of *physician satisfaction* translates to a better bottom line. Staff and physician satisfaction surveys can identify areas that need improvement.

- Payers – Payers have a keen interest in the status of the organization. *Payer satisfaction* deals with the value for payers' investment and the organization's employee satisfaction with the service provided. Payers are also interested in quality outcomes, and benefit coordinators want to know that employees receive high-quality care.

Culture of Safety and Continued Quality Improvement

Quality improvement is the informed, researched activities that aim to create a direct improvement for delivering healthcare. To foster a culture of safety and continued quality improvement, the nurse executive must employee structure measures that evaluate the quality of resources, availability, and accessibility (bed capacity, health insurance, and staffing). Also, it is vital for him/her to employ process measures that determine healthcare service delivery (guidelines and protocols) and outcome assessments that denote the final results (mortality, patient satisfaction, and improved health status).

Measurements of QI

QI efforts should be quantifiably assessed to demonstrate if those efforts result in modification of the desired endpoint and in the intended direction and to evaluate any unintentional consequences that require additional efforts. The rationale for measurement of QI efforts is that quality practices are reflected in good performance and by improving this performance, better quality will result. One of the challenges of measuring healthcare is association between variability and decision making, problem solving, and high-level cognitive reasoning.

The AHRQ and the Joint Commission are just two of the organizations that recommend using reliable and valid patient safety and quality measures. AHRQ's National Quality Measures Clearinghouse contains many of these measures at: http://www.qualitymeasures.ahrq.gov. The process of developing the measures involves reviewing literature, evaluating reliability and validity, determining how to use the measure, and testing the measure. In healthcare, benchmarking continuously and collaboratively measures and compares the outcome of chief work activities with the outcomes of leaders in the field.

Evidence-Based Practice Implications

From a comprehensive review of improvement strategies and projects, Hughes (2013) identified several practice implications associated with the methodological rigor and generalizability of *evidence-based practice*.[8] These include:

- The importance of having *strong leadership commitment*, and support cannot be overstated. Leadership needs to empower staff, be actively involved, and continuously drive quality improvement. Without the commitment and support of senior-level leadership, even the best intended projects are at great risk of being unsuccessful. Champions of the quality initiative and quality improvement must exist throughout the organization, especially in leadership positions and on the management team.

- A *culture of safety and improvement* that rewards improvement and is driven to improve quality is important. The culture is needed to support a quality infrastructure that has the resources and human capital required for successfully improving quality.

- Quality improvement teams must have the right *stakeholders* involved.

- Due to the complexity of healthcare, *multidisciplinary teams and strategies* are essential. Multidisciplinary teams from participating centers/units must work

---

[8] "EPC Topic Nomination and Selection," U.S. Department of Health & Human Services, Agency for Healthcare Research and Quality, http://www.ahrq.gov/research/findings/evidence-based-reports/topic-nomination/index.html

closely together, taking advantage of communication strategies such as face-to-face meetings, conference calls, and dedicated email listservs, and must use the guidance of trained facilitators and expert faculty throughout the process of implementing change initiatives, when possible.

- Quality improvement teams and stakeholders must *understand the problem and root causes*. There must be a consensus on the definition of the problem. To this end, a clearly defined and universally agreed upon metric is essential. This agreement is as crucial as the validity of the data to the success of any improvement effort.

- Use a *proven, methodologically sound approach* without being distracted by the jargon used in quality improvement. The importance given to using clear models, terms, and processes is critical, especially because many of the quality tools are interrelated; using only one tool will not produce successful results.

- *Standardizing care processes* and ensuring that everyone uses those standards should improve processes by making them more efficient and effective and improve organizational and patient outcomes.

- *Evidence-based practice* can facilitate ongoing quality improvement efforts.

- Implementation plans must be *flexible* to adapt to needed changes as they develop.

- Efforts to change practice and improve the quality of care can have *multiple purposes* including redesigning care processes to maximize efficiency and effectiveness, improving customer satisfaction, improving patient outcomes, and improving organizational climate.

- *Appropriate use of technology* can improve team functioning, foster collaboration, reduce human error, and improve patient safety.

- Efforts must have *sufficient resources* including protected staff time.

- *Continually collect and analyze data and communicate results* on critical indicators across the organization. The ultimate goal of assessing and monitoring quality is to use findings to assess performance and define other areas needing improvement.

- *Change takes time*, so it is important to stay focused and persevere.

Assessing Results of Care Delivery

Nursing Sensitive Indicators

Nursing sensitive indicators (NDNQI indicators) are associated with the nursing care process, structure, and outcomes. Facets of nursing care, for example, intervention and assessment, are measured with the use of *process indicators. Structure indicators* measure the nursing staff's supply and levels of education, certification, and skills. *Outcome indicators* are specific to patient outcomes or quality of nursing care such as intravenous infiltrations or falls.

Nursing sensitive indicators are developed using the following steps:
- Review peer-reviewed literature to identify indicators that are nursing sensitive
- Speak with topic experts to identify measurement issues and collect additional information
- Develop a plan for data collection and reporting
- Conduct pilot studies to test data collection guidelines and forms
- Revise plan for data collection and reporting
- Develop a web data collection system
- Announce the availability of a new indicator
- Conduct data analysis and develop quarterly reports

NDNQI posts a list of nursing sensitive indicators on the National Quality Forum. Among the top indicators are nursing hours per patient day, nursing turnover, patient falls, injury level, pressure ulcer rate, and community-acquired infections.

ORYX Indicators

The Joint Commission introduced the ORYX initiative in 1997. This is part of the accreditation process that integrates outcomes and other performance improvement data. ORYX measurement requirements reinforce Joint Commission-accredited healthcare facilities in their efforts to improve. They also provide an aim for improvement that directs and accompanies the standards-based survey process.

National Patient Safety Goals

National Patient Safety Goals (NPSGs), relevant to the practice area, were issued in 2013 by the Joint Commission. These areas include office-based surgery, long-term care, laboratory services, hospitals, home care, behavioral healthcare, and ambulatory care. These NPSGs are available at:

http://www.jointcommission.org/standards_information/npsgs.aspx. The purpose of these goals is to achieve patient safety.

Chapter 3: Transformational Leadership

This chapter covers issues of transformational leadership, such as leadership effectiveness, ethics, and advocacy.

LEADERSHIP EFFECTIVENESS

To be an effective leader in today's healthcare environment, a nurse must have the ability to demonstrate strong leadership skills by building interpersonal relationships with board members, chief executives, physicians, and staff. This is done through effective communication, collaboration, decision making, and evaluation. Also, a nurse leader must provide strategic direction to nurses and nurse managers, have an operational understanding to carry out cost-saving principles, and have the ability to foster relationship competencies.

Mission and Philosophy

Both the mission and vision of an organization align with the facility's structural intent. The philosophy of a healthcare facility instills confidence in those who seek care from that institution.

Purpose

The *mission statement* of a healthcare facility provides a general statement about its purpose. A *vision statement* describes the organization's goals and aspirations. These statements are meant to motivate and inspire those who are affiliated with the healthcare facility, and they are future-oriented and address what the facility plans to do given its resources. Progressive organizations usually have more defined and comprehensive mission statements. Most of these involve statements about the staff and administration (Rundio & Wilson, 2010).

Organization Models

Organizations are structured in several ways. Some *organization models* are:

- Vertical integration – Gives different, but complementary services to all parties such as the affiliate of an HMO and a hospital.

- Horizontal integration – Shares services across two or more organizations such as the provision of oncology services by one and the provision of orthopedic services by the other.

- Shared governance – Fosters ownership of completed work by involvement of workers in decisions about staffing, performance, structure, and resource allocation.

- Joint venture – One partner provides a service, and the other partner provides financing.

- Functional model – Decision making is centralized with a lack of coordination.

- Matrix model – Integrates functions and products, violating the unity-of-command principle.

Planning

The planning process includes performing assessments, setting goals, establishing objectives, and determining actions. Three forms of planning are:

Strategic Planning
Strategic planning is the development of an organizational strategy that will provide a long-term road map for a healthcare facility. This process is extremely important in our current economy, as it is a set of processes that identify the desired future of the organization. Strategic planning provides a map of how an organization will achieve its goals and objectives and is a powerful team-building strategy. Additionally, it creates the necessary enthusiasm for future change, action, and market improvement.

Contingency Planning
Contingency planning involves managing the business and determining what should be done before, during, and after an unexpected occurrence such as a tornado or earthquake. Also, the *contingency plan* is the way the healthcare facility operates on a day-to-day basis.

Program Planning
Program planning is the organization's capacity to successfully execute a plan or service. With this process, programs must match the organization's philosophy and

beliefs to create a profit for the healthcare facility. Some programs are mandated, such as mental health services, whereas others are voluntary, such as women's health services.

Healthy Work Environment

A *healthy work environment* directly impacts organizational performance, patient outcomes, staff retention, and satisfaction. Many healthcare organizations and nursing associations use criteria to outline healthy work environment. Nine main elements, as the Nursing Organizations Alliance issued, can help in developing a healthy work environment. These are:

- Recognition of meaningful practice contributions by nurses
- Recognition of the profession's value and contribution
- Encouragement of professional practice and continued growth and development
- Collaborative decision-making
- Clear, expert, credible, and competent leadership
- Appropriate supply of qualified nurses on staff
- Accountable culture
- Culture of communication
- Culture of collaboration

Leadership Concepts, Principles, and Styles

Contemporary Leadership Theories

The complexity of today's healthcare environment demands that the nurse leader be flexible and adaptable. The six new concepts of leadership that support flexibility and adaptability are:

- <u>Charismatic Leadership</u> – These leaders have the ability to engage others with the power of their personalities. They inspire emotional connection and use charisma to advance revolutionary ideas.

- <u>Connective Leadership</u> – These leaders draw on their ability to bring others together to facilitate change. They recognize that obtaining results through cooperation, collaboration, collegiality, and coordination is more effective than independent leadership.

- Shared Leadership – This concept is based on empowerment of others. These leaders recognize the importance of informal and formal leadership. Shared governance and teamwork epitomize the philosophy of shared leadership.

- Servant Leadership – These leaders put other people and their needs before his/her own. Servant leaders choose to lead by serving the interests of others.

- Transactional Leadership – This concept is derived from the principles of social-exchange theory. This theory implies that social, psychological, and political benefits exist in all relationships such as that of the leader and follower.

- Transformational Leadership – This concept involves the principle that leaders transform the healthcare facility through cultural and contextual changes. These leaders encourage taking risks and support an atmosphere of trust and self-actualization.

Trait Theory

Trait theory focuses on the individual characteristics of the leader, which are considered the leader's traits. These leaders possess certain traits that result in success. These include creative problem solving, drive, persistence, initiative, resilience, tolerance, self-confidence, and intelligence.

Behavioral Theory

The focus of *behavioral theory* is on the style of practice, which is considered the leader's behavior. Autocratic leaders attempt to change the behavior of subordinates through external control by coercion, punishment, authority, and power. Democratic leaders focus on changing subordinates through participation, involvement in goal setting, and collaboration. Permissive leaders assume that subordinates can make their own decisions and need little direction or facilitation. Finally, bureaucratic leaders rely on healthcare facility policies and rules to control and influence subordinates.

Appreciative Inquiry

According to Bushe (2013), *appreciative inquiry* is about the co-evolutionary search for the best in employees, their organizations, and their environment. It focuses on the systematic discovery of what gives meaning to a living system and what is capable in ecological, economical, and human terms. Appreciative inquiry utilizes the study and change of social systems with collective inquiry of what could be or is the best, along with using persuasion, incentives, and coercion to plan change. Faculty and students of the Department of Organizational Behavior at Case Western Reserve University developed this theory in the 1980s.

Initiating and Managing Change

The theories that are considered change models are:

Maslow's Hierarchy of Needs Theory

With *Maslow's Hierarchy of Needs Theory*, there are five basic concepts: self-actualization, esteem of status, affiliation or acceptance, security or safety, and physiological needs. These categories of basic needs are common to all people, and the hierarchy is an arrangement that ranks the concepts from lowest to highest. To achieve success, the person must meet the needs at the lower levels before he/she tackles the next levels.

Herzberg's Two-Factor Theory

Herzberg's Two-Factor Theory defines workplace factors that contribute to job satisfaction and another factor set that leads to dissatisfaction. The fundamentals of this change theory are that attitudes and their connection with employee mental health are related to Maslow's theory of motivation. Individuals are not content with lower-order needs in the workplace such as those associated with minimum salary levels and safe working conditions. Rather, people look for gratification at higher-level needs such as recognition, advancement, and achievement.

Lewin's Equilibrium Theory

Lewin proposed that people maintain a state of equilibrium by balancing restraining and driving forces within any field. For this to occur, there must be a disruption of balance. To lessen the power of restraining forces, one must either increase the force or decrease the power of the force. The first phase of this process in *Lewin's Equilibrium Theory* is unfreezing, where data is gathered, the problem is identified, and a decision for change is made. With the movement phase, a plan is formed, strategies are developed, and change is implemented. In the refreezing phase, the change is integrated into the organization and support is put into place to sustain the change.

Rogers' Change Theory

Rogers believed that innovations perceived by people that could have greater advantage for change should be adopted more rapidly than other innovations. Based on innovativeness, adopter categories of *Rogers' Change Theory* include: innovators (take risks), early adopters (translate innovator's message), early majority (adopt new ideas early on), late majority (adopt new ideas later on), and resistors (last to adopt an innovation).

Succession Planning

For the success of a healthcare organization, there must be future leaders who can take over when key executives leave. Strategic planning includes *succession planning*, which smoothly transitions leadership in the facility, ensures high-quality standards by working with physicians, and grooms new leaders. To address this issue, the National Center for Healthcare Leadership (NCHL, 2010) recommends best practices that emphasize:

- Clear communication stressing the importance of succession planning
- Tight linkages between succession planning and healthcare facility priorities
- Extensive involvement in the program from various levels of management
- Integrated use of a leadership competency model
- Recruitment of new employees who share the organization's values and who have the ability to develop desired competencies
- Highly customized and flexible professional development plans
- Repeated assessment of those with strong leadership potential
- Continuous evaluation of the outcomes of succession planning activities

Healthcare Employee Engagement and Empowerment

Organizational trust, in a modernized healthcare scene, comprises a vital component in defining the healthcare facility's employee commitment, performance, and retention. Laschinger, Finegan, Samian et al. (2000) examined organizational trust's and empowerment's effects on commitment, using Kanter's model of workplace *empowerment*. They found that more effective commitment and higher organizational trust was the result of empowered nurses.

Employee *engagement* is used to refer to psychological behaviors, traits, and states and to their outcomes and antecedents. Employee empowerment is a strategy and philosophy that allows employees to make decisions about their jobs and workplaces, helps employees take responsibility for their work and the results of it, and allows employees to serve patients at the organization level where patient interface exists.

ETHICS AND ADVOCACY

Professions are defined by many ethics that govern their practice. Nursing has a long history of a commitment to high ethical standards, and in 1990, the ANA started the Center for Ethics and Human Rights. This program addresses the complex ethical and human rights issues that confront many nurses, and it designs activities to increase ethical competence in the profession (Rundio & Wilson, 2010).

Ethical Principles

The three main ethical principles that guide individuals in the healthcare field are:

Respect for People

Human beings have the capacity for rational action and moral choice, and as autonomous individuals, they have value. Their judgment and choices must be respected. The degree of autonomy varies according to the person's decision-making ability (Rundio & Wilson, 2010).

Beneficence

Beneficence holds that one has an obligation to do no harm and promote good. This principle is often affected by ethical dilemmas. This applies to end-of-life decisions, continued treatment when prognosis is poor, and refusal of certain treatments and procedures (Rundio & Wilson, 2010).

Justice

Justice means that which is fair or that which is deserved. The concept of patient rights is associated with justice. One ethical issue that relates to neglecting the principle of justice is the allocation of resources (Rundio & Wilson, 2010).

Ethical Dilemmas

An *ethical dilemma* is a situation that exists in the presence of competing values in which individuals and the community have a vested interest. Because of ethical dilemmas, healthcare facilities have formed multidisciplinary ethics committees to offer advice regarding the dilemmas faced by caregivers, patients, and patients' families. To identify ethical issues, a systematic approach should be used. Components of an "ethics evaluation" include a review of medical indications, quality of life, patient preferences, and contextual issues (Rundio & Wilson, 2010).

Resource Utilization

With the allocation of scarce resources, ethical concerns can arise. Clinical ethics and organizational ethics conflict when there are diminished resources. Because nurse executives are responsible for resource utilization and allocation, they often must strike a balance between these factors.

Ethical Identification Model
- Identify the problem
- Discuss the ethical dilemma
- Gather subjective and objective data
- Look at the alternatives
- Study the consequences of these alternatives
- Select the most appropriate alternative
- Compare that alternative with the committee's value system

Advocating for Patient Access, Safety, and Rights

Advocates are those who represent or plead the cause of those who cannot speak for themselves. Nurses are often considered "patient advocates" because they serve in this role for patients. However, a nurse cannot act as a patient advocate when his/her values do not align with the patient's choice (Rundio & Wilson, 2010).

The Patient Bill of Rights

In 1973, the Patient Bill of Rights was created by the American Hospital Association (AHA). This is a list of patient rights that is issued by each state, and the state laws mandate its provision. Generally included in this Bill of Rights are the rights to:

- Considerate and respectful care
- Know about information regarding diagnosis, prognosis, and treatment
- Informed consent
- Know about alternative treatments
- Privacy
- Confidentiality regarding patient records
- Have the hospital make a reasonable response to request for services
- Know if people providing treatment have professional relationships that could affect patient care
- Be informed of human experimentation
- Refuse treatment
- Receive and examine the bill

Chapter 4: New Knowledge and Innovation

In this chapter, the nurse executive will gain a better understanding of innovation and new knowledge.

RESEARCH, KNOWLEDGE, AND EVIDENCE-BASED PRACTICE

In today's healthcare environment, there is a need for evidence-based practice and research that supports this knowledge. To obtain an environment that supports evidence-based practice, nurses must use research findings to provide the best possible nursing care. As the largest group of healthcare providers in the U.S., nurses are vital to quality care improvement and safety assurance.

Conducting Research

Research is critical to the growth of the nursing profession, and nurses must be able to use and understand data and statistical methods to conduct research relevant to patient needs, to move nursing closer to other applied fields, and to improve bedside care. The categories of research are:

- Applied – Designed to solve a practical problem or answer a question

- Basic – Tests and evaluates theories or contributes to an existing body of research

- Case Study – Investigation of a single individual or a group with similar diagnoses

- Descriptive – Reports selected variables and proves facts that are already accepted

- Developmental – Deals with changes that occur as a result of developmental growth

- Experimental – Randomly assigns participants with manipulation of variables

- Field – Conducted in the natural setting

- Historical – Explains or interprets something from the past

- Laboratory – Conducted in a setting designed for research

- Longitudinal – Measuring the same participants as they grow older

- Qualitative – Doesn't follow the scientific model, but focuses on subjective data

- Quantitative – Involves nominal, ordinal, and interval data

Institutional Review Board (IRB) Requirements

Protecting human subjects is a chief concern of nursing researchers. The *institutional review boards* (IRBs) exist to ensure that research participants are protected from unscrupulous and unethical practices and researchers. The HIPAA law that governs research involves a set of rules and regulations that add a layer of protection to the way data produced by healthcare facilities can be accessed and reported. Guidance documents are posted on the FDA website, and these guidelines area a representation of the agency's rationale for protecting human subjects in research.

Research and Evidence-Based Practice Techniques

Data

Data is either qualitative or quantitative. *Qualitative data* involves the use of words to describe concepts, facts, participant statements, and subjective observations. *Quantitative data* involves the use of numbers to enhance study precision. Three categories of quantitative data are:

- Nominal – Data is categorical and cannot be arranged in any particular order such as by marital status, religion, or race.

- Ordinal – Data is ordered, but differences such as socioeconomic status, car size, and facility ratings cannot be determined.

- Interval – Also called ratio, data in this category is ordered and has meaningful differences such as ratio data where there is an absolute zero.

Instrument Validity and Reliability

Validity means that the data-gathering instrument measures exactly what it is meant to measure, and this value is never 100%. *Reliability* is how well or how consistent an instrument is for the purpose of a particular study. While an instrument may be reliable (able to measure something several times) without being valid (appropriate), an instrument may not be valid unless it is reliable.

Translating Research into Practice

Many interventions in nursing are based on ritual, not on current evidence. The purpose of research is to learn more about the healthcare environment and to contribute to a growing body of knowledge. For a healthcare provider to translate research into practice, he/she must have a question and evidence that supports a practice change. Leaders in evidence-based practice for nursing recommend the use of "PICO" for this process. This includes:

- Patient, population, or patient population
- Intervention
- Comparative intervention
- Outcome

Research and Scholarly Inquiry

Many healthcare facilities now sponsor nursing research committees to provide assistance with grant writing, educate staff about the value of research, and foster research in the nursing profession. Nursing leaders should contribute to nursing research through grant writing, research councils, and incorporation of evidence.

Grant Writing

Academic institutions and large healthcare organizations employ grant writers who identify sources of grants, craft grant proposals, and guide the grant process. This process is known as *grant writing.* Organizations often offer small restricted grants that provide novice grant writers an opportunity to develop a modest research project and apply for necessary funding. Also, certain private agencies offer grants to many healthcare facilities. Drug companies are liberal in providing grant funds, and the researcher must disclose the association.

Research Councils

The National Advisory Council for Nursing Research (NACNR) consists of six officers from various organizations and associations and 15 members appointed by the Secretary. NACNR offers second-level grant application review and recommendation for application approval and consideration. Many associations, organizations, institutions, and healthcare facilities have *nursing research councils*, and these groups educate nurses about the importance of using research in clinical practice.

Incorporating Evidence and a Model for Change

Researchers Rosswurm and Larrabee (2007) propose that a paradigm shift from institution-driven practice to evidence-based practice was caused by an increase in medical research and accessibility to it. Research and theoretical literature related to change theory, evidence-based practice, and utilization serves as the basis for their model, which supports a combination of clinical expertise, contextual evidence, and qualitative and quantitative data. They conclude that healthcare providers require resources and skills to assess, integrate, and disseminate best evidence into nursing practice and that researchers of varying disciplines collaborating can improve innovations based on evidence.

INNOVATION

Lateral Thinking, Creativity, and Intelligent Risk-Taking

Problem solving and idea generation are two concepts that require both logical (vertical) thinking and innovative (lateral) thinking. *Lateral thinking* creates the idea, and *vertical thinking* carries the idea forward. While vertical thinking tries to overcome problems by addressing them head-on, lateral thinking tries to bypass them with a radical, new, and different approach. With lateral thinking, one recognizes that the brain has pattern recognition systems, and a person develops solutions based on previous solutions to similar problems. Lateral thinking techniques allow nurse executives and other leaders to come up with brilliant, original opportunities and solutions to various problems. Disciplined thinking is effective in making healthcare services better, but to improve existing systems, lateral thinking is necessary. *Creativity* involves thinking in both ways, but without action following it, creativity is sterile.

Leadership development is central to the modernization of the healthcare practice environment. According to experts, *intelligent risk-taking* is only one element that must be considered. Intelligent risk-taking is not only for nurse leaders. For the organization to advance, all employees must be willing to take risks. Also, risk-taking requires a great deal of support from superiors, nurse managers, and employees. It must be embedded in the corporate culture. Finally, expect to make mistakes when you take risks. Every intelligent risk-taker encounters mistakes, so a safe environment for employees to make mistakes should be considered.

Developing a Framework for Implementing Innovations

Many healthcare organizations foster innovation through serendipitous acts of creativity. Others require an unstructured approach, achieving only small incremental improvements or not successfully implementing anything. Strategic innovation has a focus on result generation using a systematic method. An innovation is "strategic" if it is a repeatable, intentional procedure leading to a notable change in the quality of care received by patients.

Dimensions of Strategic Innovation

Strategic innovation has several dimensions, which intertwine and result in growth-oriented outcomes. The *managed innovation process* is at the center of this, and it facilitates connection between the leaders and the employees. Patient insight gives leaders a "bottom-up" perspective and allows for the understanding of both stated (articulated) and unrecognized (unarticulated) needs of potential and actual patients. Strategic relationships and technologies are just some of the assets and aptitudes that can influence the quality of care that patients receive. With the strategic innovation process, internal capabilities and other dimensions of an organization give the organization a capacity to be effective and a readiness to act. This process is designed to facilitate strategic alignment, which focuses on goals and builds enthusiasm among the key stakeholders.

Strategic innovation includes eight dimensions:

- <u>Sustainable innovation</u> – Is a forum for continuing competitive advantage

- <u>Disciplined implementation</u> – Requires inspiration to impact business

- <u>Organizational readiness</u> – Involves the capacity to act

- <u>Core technologies and competencies</u> – Involves using corporate assets as leverage

- Patient insight – Helps understand unarticulated and articulated patient needs

- Industry foresight – Helps understand rising trends

- Strategic alignment – Acquires support internally

- Managed innovation process – Combines strategic approaches of a traditional and non-traditional nature

Phases of Strategic Innovation

The strategic innovation approach combines both traditional and unconventional elements and involves the "all things possible" perspective. A team-based framework brings together a cross-functional team. The overall approach involves two distinct stages: convergence and divergence. The *divergence phase* is strategic innovation's center; possesses traits of exploration, open-endedness, inquisitiveness; and entails the use of creative thought and techniques that envision the future. Quantitatively exploring market and industry inclinations as well as researching patient insight can be a part of this phase. The *convergence phase* involves conventional development and planning for business, where opportunities are selected, assessed, cultivated, and executed.

Steps to Successful Implementation

To implement strategic innovation, two things are necessary: cultural readiness and operational readiness. *Cultural readiness* describes a healthcare facility's readiness to embrace innovation based on its philosophy and culture. This involves factors including: innovative mindset, business boundaries and thinking, internal power tensions, bureaucracy levels, decision-making styles, and political agendas. *Operational readiness* involves factors including efficient practices and procedures related to business, appropriate technological and organizational infrastructure, available funds, and qualified staff. These factors can determine a facility's capacity to act.

The steps for successful implementation are:
- Step 1 – Application of Strategic Innovation Principles: During this step, the nurse leader must employ strategic innovation principles continuously, even into the convergence phase.

- Step 2 – Implementation of Skillsets and Mindsets: At various strategic innovation process stages, different mindsets and skills are required.

- Step 3 – Momentum: The strategic innovation process could grind to a halt without continued energy and enthusiasm. To maintain momentum, it is imperative to use strategic alignment to create a strong basis for cross-organizational stakeholder support. Also, a nurse leader should leverage implementation-related best practices and keep the initiative visible.

- Step 4 – A Formal Project Management Approach: For quality outcomes, strategic thinking must be converted to doable projects. During this stage, the efforts of strategic innovation must take the form of multiple "daughter" projects. This recommends that project management, such as resource allocation, realistic expectations, and performance goals, be made a focus.

- Step 5 – Understanding Organizational Priorities: Awareness of the healthcare facility's priorities is essential as is ensuring that all leaders continue to support the initiatives of the strategic innovation process.

Leveraging Diversity

According to the U.S. Department of Health and Human Services (2013e), the definition of *leveraging diversity* is fostering "an inclusive workplace where diversity and individual differences are valued and leveraged to achieve the vision and mission of the organization." The key elements and behaviors of leveraging diversity are:[9]
- Recruitment, development, and retention of a diverse, high-quality workforce in an equitable manner
- Leading and managing an inclusive workforce that maximizes the talents of each person to acquire sound business results
- Development of policies and procedures that encourage cultural awareness and acceptance
- Respect and understanding of individual differences to achieve the goals and objectives of the organization
- Development and use of measures and rewards to hold others and yourself accountable for achieving results that embrace diversity
- Use of cultural awareness to resolve conflicts

---

[9] "Leadership Competencies," U.S. Department of Health of Human Services, accessed November 11, 2015, http://hhsu.learning.hhs.gov/competencies/leadership-lev_diversity.asp.

- Use of an understanding of cultural differences to influence others and to manage across cultures

Evaluating and Applying Technology to Support Practice Innovation

In a study done by Westbrook and Associates (2009), researchers sought to assess the factors that allow healthcare organizations to harness *information and communication technologies* (ICT). Adoption of ICT is a key strategy in meeting the challenges that face most healthcare systems internationally due to rising costs, increased demands, and limited resources. Regardless of ICT investment by healthcare facilities, acceptance has been slower, and benefits are not as expected.

In her blog *Physician Practice* (2012), Marisa Torrieri wrote that 2012 brought about some of the most important developments in healthcare technology. On her list were:

- Patient portals – These are a secure alternative for healthcare provider-patient communication.

- Cloud-based technology – This is a great way for small practices to reduce overhead and difficulties by outsourcing the maintenance of data.

- Apps – Used for patient engagement, these are used to regulate discussions on patient portals. Now, they also help patients take control of healthcare.

- Tablet computing – This is smartphone and tablet versions of electronic health records.

- Speech-recognition tools – Voice-recognition tools increase the ease of documentation.

- Twitter – Social media is used to promote healthcare facilities and physician practices.

- Secure messaging – This meets HIPAA privacy and security requirements.

- Video – Video-based telemedicine has increased due to the growth in coverage by private payers in many states.

- <u>Accountable care organizations (ACOs)</u> – Introduced by the federal government, ACOs are not in healthcare facilities or independent practices.

Test Your Knowledge

1. Under the Americans with Disabilities Act, reasonable accommodations implies all of the following modifications EXCEPT:
   A. Modifications to the job application process that allow a qualified individual with a disability to be considered for a certain position
   B. Modifications that enable an employee with a disability to profit from the same privileges and benefits as those without disabilities
   C. Modifications to the work environment circumstances, or manner under which the position is held, that allow a qualified person with a disability to perform the necessary work functions
   D. Modifications that enable an employee with a disability to achieve certain privileges and benefits because of his/her disabilities

2. Under the Fair Labor Standards Act, a workweek is a regularly occurring period of _____ hours during seven consecutive 24-hour periods.
   A. 40
   B. 140
   C. 168
   D. 175

3. The Fair Labor Standards Act does NOT require and enforce which of the following?
   A. Employer record keeping
   B. Breaks and meal periods
   C. Minimum wage
   D. Overtime pay

4. Which agency or law requires that men and women who perform equal work receive equal pay?
   A. FLSA Amendments of 1989
   B. Equal Pay Act of 1963
   C. Civil Rights Act of 1964
   D. Rehabilitation Act of 1973

5. Under the FLSA Child Labor Provisions law, the basic minimum age for employment is _____ years.
    A. 14
    B. 15
    C. 16
    D. 18

6. Which of the following employers are NOT subject to anti-discrimination laws under the Civil Rights Act of 1964, which is enforced by the Equal Employment Opportunity Commission?
    A. Those with 20 or fewer employees
    B. Paid volunteers
    C. Non-citizens of the U.S. who are employed overseas by U.S. employers
    D. Independent contractors

7. Which of the following issues would NOT qualify as an exception to the Civil Rights Act under the bonafide occupational qualification?
    A. Mobility problems
    B. Weight-bearing difficulties
    C. Trouble lifting
    D. Seasonal depression

8. Who is protected under the Age Discrimination in Employment Act of 1967?
    A. All American workers
    B. Individuals between the ages of 16 and 35
    C. Individuals between the ages of 40 and 70
    D. Individuals under the age of 16

9. Which corporate culture type is characterized by a "top-down" concept, with decisions made at the executive level and passed on to employees?
    A. Autocratic
    B. Bureaucratic
    C. Democratic
    D. Participative

10. All of the following statements are true concerning the Occupational Safety and Health Administration EXCEPT:
    A. OSHA covers any employer who operates or engages in a business that affects commerce.
    B. OSHA is authorized by the federal government to conduct a workplace inspection on any business.
    C. The U.S. Department of Labor governs OSHA.
    D. OSHA can conduct inspections in response to an employee complaint.

11. The Occupational Safety and Health Administration requires employers with _____ or more employees to keep records of work-related illnesses and injuries.
    A. 7
    B. 10
    C. 11
    D. 14

12. According to the current statistics reported by the Occupational Health and Safety Administration, at which rate has occupational and workplace injury and illness declined?
    A. 50%
    B. 57%
    C. 60%
    D. 67%

13. Which OSHA cooperative program is for employers with special interest and experience in job safety and health who also have a commitment to improving workplace safety?
    A. Alliance Program
    B. Voluntary Protection Program
    C. Strategic Partnership Program
    D. Challenge Program

14. Which sequence would represent an appropriate chain of command in the healthcare environment?
    A. Nurse Executive, RN Team Leader, Staff RN, CNA
    B. Nurse Executive, CNA, Staff RN, RN Team Leader
    C. CNA, Staff RN, RN Team Leader, Nurse Executive
    D. Nurse Executive, Director of Nursing, Chief Executive Officer, Hospital Board

15. Of the following people, who is NOT mandated by state law to report neglect and abuse of children and/or the elderly?
    A. Social workers
    B. Teachers
    C. Nurses
    D. Medical billers

16. Which of the following is NOT a cause of health disparities?
    A. Lack of education
    B. Poverty
    C. Environmental threats
    D. Occupation

17. Which is the most accurate description of lateral violence?
    A. Lateral violence is a form of harassment where nurses show aggressive or destructive behavior against each other or one group against a person or group.
    B. Lateral violence is a form of physical violence where one nurse assaults another.
    C. Lateral violence is a form of physical violence where a group of nurses assault one other person.
    D. Lateral violence is a form of harassment where the nurse executive shows aggressive or destructive behavior against his/her superiors.

18. Which type of network system involves direct communication in all directions without restriction?
    A. Centralized system
    B. Decentralized system
    C. Restricted system
    D. Unrestricted system

19. Which form of electronic data transfer is considered a first-level product that brings together data from other sources and delivers it electronically to the user?
    A. Computerized Medical Record System (CMRS)
    B. Electronic Medical Record (EMR)
    C. Electronic Patient Record (EPR)
    D. Automated Medical Record (AMR)

20. Which process of the regulation of the nursing profession is the process of granting permission to a person to practice?
    A. Certification
    B. Licensure
    C. Credentialing
    D. Registration

21. What is the purpose of the Joint Commission?
    A. To accredit acute care hospitals, critical access facilities, medical equipment services, home healthcare and hospice agencies, rehabilitation centers, physician practices, surgical centers, skilled nursing homes, and independent laboratories
    B. To set the standards for healthcare facilities and organizations
    C. Both A and B
    D. Neither A nor B

22. What is the difference between the Medicare and Medicaid programs?
    A. The Medicare program was an addendum to the Medicaid program.
    B. The Medicare program was aimed at the retirement age population and those with disabilities, whereas the Medicaid program was established for low-income children and their parents or guardians; those with developmental disabilities; and other low-income groups such as pregnant women, the elderly, and children.
    C. The Medicaid program was aimed at the retirement age population and those with disabilities, whereas the Medicare program was established for low-income children and their parents or guardians; those with developmental disabilities; and other low-income groups such as pregnant women, the elderly, and children.
    D. The Medicare program was created to replace the Medicaid program.

23. Which model was designed to provide direction for healthcare, allow multidisciplinary teams to communicate and collaborate, and define intended outcomes following the law of averages and evidence-based research?
    A. Shared governance model
    B. Traditional hierarchy
    C. Clinical pathways
    D. Career ladders

24. Which healthcare delivery model is a task-oriented method in which individual caregivers perform specific assigned tasks for all patients in a given unit or area?
   A. Case Method Nursing
   B. Team Nursing
   C. Functional Nursing
   D. Primary Nursing

25. What is the purpose of certification?
   A. To assure the public and concerned parties that a person has mastered skills and knowledge in a certain area
   B. To designate when institutions or individuals have met the established standards set by an organization
   C. To accept the credentialing status of another credentialing body for specified purposes
   D. To show legal recognition of professional practice

26. Which of the following is NOT an aspect considered under the ANA Standards of Professional Performance?
   A. Ethics
   B. Research
   C. Education
   D. Diagnosis

27. Nurse Practice Acts (NPAs) are regulated on which level?
   A. Local
   B. State
   C. Federal
   D. None of the above

28. The four predictable stages of group development are:
   A. Team formation, team building, team structure, and team elimination
   B. Forming, storming, norming, and performing
   C. Starting, gathering, producing, evaluating
   D. Primary, secondary, tertiary, and quaternary

29. The Joint Commission's standard HR.01.04.01 requires hospitals and healthcare facilities to:
    A. Offer an orientation program that is 3 days long for temporary staff and 4-12 weeks long for long-term employees
    B. Offer a general facility orientation and a unit-specific orientation
    C. Offer a unit-specific orientation
    D. Offer a general facility orientation

30. Which is NOT true concerning competency validation during orientation?
    A. The Joint Commission standard HR.01.06.01 requires that staff competency be assessed and documented during orientation.
    B. Many worksites complete competency validation initially via a checklist.
    C. One competency validation tool is the Performance Based Development System (PBDS).
    D. Competency checklists are completely accurate concerning each person's perception of his/her abilities.

31. There is an accepted process that occurs in all areas of life and learning, which is defined as a purposeful, goal-directed, self-regulatory process that is context bound. What is this called?
    A. Cultural competence
    B. Critical thinking
    C. Leveraging diversity
    D. All three terms are interchangeable.

32. Conflict between two nurses who work in the same intensive care unit is called _____ conflict.
    A. Intergroup
    B. Intragroup
    C. Interpersonal
    D. Intrapersonal

33. A nurse executive knows that a person is upset based on his/her voice and facial expression. This is considered to be which element of emotional intelligence?
    A. Perceiving emotions
    B. Using emotions
    C. Managing emotions
    D. Understanding emotions

34. Which concept in healthcare focuses on the continuous and systematic actions that result in a measurable improvement in the health of patient populations and healthcare services?
    A. The Plan-Do-Study-Act (PDSA) cycle
    B. Quality improvement (QI)
    C. Communication systems
    D. None of the above

35. Which type of system interacts with the environment and internally?
    A. Closed system
    B. Open system
    C. Input system
    D. Output system

36. The nurse executive is discussing the use of a new electronic data transfer system during a staff meeting. One staff nurse asks a question, and the nurse leader explains a concept to that employee. When the staff nurse repeats back what she hears to the nurse executive, which type of communication has occurred?
    A. Interviewing
    B. Two-way communication
    C. Reflective communication
    D. Active listening

37. The preferred communication style in the healthcare environment is:
    A. Persuasive style
    B. Assertive style
    C. Passive style
    D. Both A and B
    E. Both B and C

38. Which of the following is a structured method for analyzing serious adverse events and detecting underlying problems that increase the likelihood of errors?
    A. Benchmarking
    B. Report cards
    C. Root cause analysis (RCA)
    D. Functional status

39. Suppose nursing researchers found that the misadministration of potassium chloride caused 100 preventable deaths in the U.S. healthcare system in 2013. What is this error considered to be?
    A. Nursing sensitive indicator
    B. Process indicator
    C. Structure indicator
    D. Sentinel event

40. Which type of healthcare improvement involves continually increasing quality to help healthcare facilities focus on vital interventions that have the greatest effect on health outcomes?
    A. Performance improvement (PI)
    B. Total quality management (TQM)
    C. Continuous quality improvement (CQI)
    D. Stakeholder satisfaction

41. Which type of indicators are part of the accreditation process of the Joint Commission that supplement and guide the standards-based survey process by providing a targeted basis for monitoring performance?
    A. Process indicators
    B. Structure indicators
    C. ORYX indicators
    D. Outcome indicators

42. What is the difference between a mission statement and a vision statement?
    A. A vision statement provides a general statement about the healthcare facility's purpose, and a mission statement describes the organization's goals and aspirations.
    B. A mission statement provides a general statement about the healthcare facility's purpose, and a vision statement describes the organization's goals and aspirations.
    C. The terms are used interchangeably.
    D. None of the above

43. A surgeon and a businessman open a surgical center. The surgeon will do the work, and the businessman will provide financing. Which type of organizational model is this?
    A. Vertical integration
    B. Horizontal integration
    C. Shared governance
    D. Joint venture

44. Which type of planning involves managing the business and determining what should be done before, during, and after an unexpected occurrence such as a tornado or earthquake?
    A. Strategic planning
    B. Contingency planning
    C. Program planning
    D. Healthy work environment

45. A nurse executive chooses not to attend a conference and instead uses the travel expense fund to buy his/her staff new uniforms. Which type of leader is this nurse executive?
    A. Charismatic leader
    B. Connective leader
    C. Servant leader
    D. Transactional leader

46. Concerning the behavior theory, which type of leader assumes that his/her subordinates can make their own decisions and that the staff need little direction?
    A. Autocratic
    B. Democratic
    C. Bureaucratic
    D. Permissive

47. Which change theory proposes that people maintain a state of equilibrium by balancing restraining and driving forces within any field?
    A. The Two-Factor Theory
    B. Maslow's Hierarchy of Needs Theory
    C. Lewin's Equilibrium Theory
    D. Rogers' Change Theory

48. Which type of planning provides smooth leadership transition for the organization to work with physicians to ensure high-quality standards and to groom new leaders?
    A. Contingency planning
    B. Succession planning
    C. Strategic planning
    D. Financial planning

49. During a nursing research project, you and your colleagues investigate a group of patients with community-acquired pneumonia. Which type of research is this?
    A. Applied research
    B. Case study research
    C. Descriptive research
    D. Experimental research

50. You are doing an observational research study regarding emergency and trauma nursing. This research is conducted in a natural setting, which is the emergency department. Which type of research is this?
    A. Field research
    B. Historical research
    C. Laboratory research
    D. Longitudinal research

51. Which group or agency ensures that research participants are protected from unethical and unscrupulous practices and researchers?
    A. Food and Drug Administration
    B. National Advisory Council for Nursing Research (NACNR)
    C. Institutional Review Board (IRB)
    D. Nursing Research Council

52. In a research report, you read that patients were listed by socioeconomic status. You understand that this data is ordered, but differences cannot be determined. Which type of data is this?
    A. Interval
    B. Ordinal
    C. Nominal
    D. Qualitative

53. Complete the following statement: An instrument _____.
    A. can be reliable without being valid.
    B. can be valid without being reliable.
    C. cannot be reliable if it is valid.
    D. cannot be valid if it is reliable.

54. There are several dimensions of strategic innovation, which are intertwined to produce growth-oriented results. Which dimension helps understand emerging trends?
    A. Strategic alignment
    B. Industry foresight
    C. Patient insight
    D. Organizational readiness

55. Which phase of the strategic innovation approach has exploratory and open-ended characteristics?
    A. Emergence phase
    B. Divergence phase
    C. Convergence phase
    D. None of the above

56. Equal employment laws involve various aspects of discrimination due to all of the following EXCEPT:
    A. Color/race/ethnicity
    B. Religion
    C. Age
    D. Sex
    E. Socioeconomic status

57. Considering the following, which benefit is not covered under the Workers' Compensation law?
    A. Medical coverage
    B. Costs of rehabilitation
    C. A percentage of wages or salary
    D. Bonus compensation for minor injury

58. An agreement negotiated between a labor union and an employer that sets forth the terms of employment for labor union workers is called:
    A. Grievance
    B. Arbitration
    C. Collective bargaining
    D. Contract

59. Why should a nurse executive demand a contract with the healthcare facility where she is employed?
    A. A contract will protect the nursing professional financially and secure job status.
    B. Contracts define the responsibilities and liabilities of employees, contractors, and/or other service providers.
    C. A contract will help the nurse secure a position that can otherwise be eliminated or restructured in the healthcare environment.
    D. All of the above

60. Which of the following is a way of thinking that allows the nurse executive to come up with original ideas and creative solutions to various problems?
    A. Critical thinking
    B. Lateral thinking
    C. Vertical thinking
    D. Logical thinking

61. A surgical team is reimbursed with one large sum for all services provided during a procedure. This is an example of _____.
    A. Fee for service payment
    B. Pay for performance
    C. Pay for coordination
    D. Bundled payment

62. Hours per patient day (HPPD) are calculated by:
    A. Dividing total production hours by the number of patient days
    B. Dividing number of patient days by the total production hours
    C. Dividing the total annual patient days by 365
    D. Dividing the number of days in one year by the total annual patient days

63. What is the purpose of amortization?
   A. It allows for easy calculation of profit or loss.
   B. It is an assignment of costs to a capital item for its lifetime, so there can be development of a replacement strategy.
   C. It measures inpatient volume based on the number of occupied beds or number of patients.
   D. All of the above

64. Which of the following statements concerning Healthy People 2020 is NOT true?
   A. Healthy People creates benchmarks to measure the impact of preventive activities.
   B. Healthy People reflects input from only one prestigious organization.
   C. Healthy People is a 10-year agenda working to improve the health of the nation.
   D. Healthy People aims to increase public awareness of the determinants of disability and disease.

65. Of the following health disparities, which were found in the recent report by the Agency for Healthcare Research and Quality?
   A. The access to care of poor people is worse than that of high-income people.
   B. Blacks, American Indians, Asians, Native Alaskans, and Hispanics received worse care than Whites.
   C. A 2 percent increase occurred between 2002 and 2009 of Americans who had difficulties accessing healthcare. The percentage grew from 24 percent to 26 percent in that time.
   D. All of the above

66. What does the Affordable Care Act of 2010 contain?
   A. It calls for the establishment of the Patient-Centered Outcomes Research Institute, which studies comparative effectiveness research.
   B. It allows the FDA to approve generic drugs.
   C. It has programs that increase incentives to provide collaborative and quality healthcare.
   D. All of the above

67. A nurse executive discovers that the physicians he/she works for are engaged in an abuse of authority and gross waste of funds. Which law would protect this nurse who plans to report the misconduct?
  A. Health Insurance Portability and Accountability Act
  B. Whistleblower Protection Act
  C. Civil Rights Act
  D. Fair Labor Standards Act

68. Which organization developed HCAHPS?
  A. Agency for Healthcare Research and Quality (AHRQ)
  B. Centers for Medicare and Medicaid Services (CMS)
  C. Both A and B
  D. Neither A nor B

69. Which type of network involves many local networks with connections that are affected by specialized networking software?
  A. Decentralized system
  B. Centralized system
  C. Wide area network
  D. Local area network

70. Which type of legislation allows licensed nurses to practice in additional states without having to apply for a second license?
  A. Nurse compact legislation
  B. Federal legislation
  C. State legislation
  D. Recognition legislation

Test Your Knowledge—Answers

1. **D.**

   According to the EEOC, reasonable accommodation means modifications that enable an employee with a disability to achieve the same privileges and benefits as those who do not have disabilities. It does not guarantee privileges or benefits because of the disability.

2. **C.**

   The FLSA sets a minimum wage below which no covered employee may be legally employed, but the law sets a maximum number of hours in a workweek. A workweek consists of a regularly reoccurring 168-hour period occurring within seven consecutive periods of 24 hours. Hours worked encompasses all of an employee's on-duty hours on the employer's premises or at the designated worksite and all the time the employee must work for the employer.

3. **B.**

   The FLSA does mandate that employers give meal period or breaks to employees, but some states implement these requirements. The other choices (A, C, and D) are all things that the FLSA does require.

4. **B.**

   The Equal Pay Act (EPA) of 1964 prohibits discrimination based on gender regarding compensation for work services. The U.S. Labor Department's Wage and Hour Division implemented amendments to the Fair Labor Standards Act (FLSA) in 1989 requiring employees lacking basic skills to receive additional remedial training in addition to their 40-hour work week. Under the Civil Rights Act of 1964, employers cannot discriminate against an employee based on factors not related to job qualifications, such as age, sexual preference, religion, race, sex, or national origin. The Rehabilitation Act of 1973 ensures that qualified individuals with handicaps are not excluded from participation in various programs and activities, or denied benefits from the employer.

5. **C.**

   The FLSA Child Labor Provisions law states that the basic minimum age for employment, which is 16 years. However, employment of 14 and 15 year old youths is allowed for certain occupations and under specific.

6. **D.**
Employers who are not subject to anti-discrimination laws include:
- those with 15 or fewer employees (not 20: choice A)
- joint labor-management committees that control job training programs
- labor organizations
- independent contractors
- unpaid volunteers (not paid volunteers: choice B)
- non-citizens employed overseas by U.S. employers (not U.S. citizens: choice C)

7. **D.**
This Civil Rights Act corrects injustices and bias through affirmative action and other mechanisms. This permits employers from "screening out" certain people who are qualified for employment. One exception to this act is bonafide occupational qualification (BFOQ), where certain challenges are more difficult or unattainable due to age. BFOQs include weight-bearing and mobility issues, such as stairs, lifting, and other physical challenges.

8. **C.**
Congress enacted the Age Discrimination in Employment Act (ADEA) in 1967 to prevent arbitrary age discrimination in regards to employment, assists employers and workers discover ways to solve problems arising from the impact of age on employment. Individuals protect by ADEA include those who are between the ages of 40 and 70 years.

9. **A.**
With the autocratic culture, managers and supervisors must enforce the decisions and help staff accept various decisions and changes. Techniques of an autocratic organization include coercion, direction of actions, and threats of punishment. In many organizations, the success of the facility depends on autocracy. A bureaucratic culture relies on rules, regulations, procedures, and policies. A participative culture is characterized by openness to recommendations and suggestions from all levels within the facility for the purpose of decision making. There is no democratic culture considered.

10. **B.**
OSHA is authorized to conduct workplace inspection on each business that is covered by the OSHA act. The U.S. Department of Labor is the federal department that governs OSHA. This organization allows OSHA to conduct an inspection at the request of the employer or in response to an employee complaint. The other choices (A, C, and D) are all correct statements.

11. **C.**

OSHA requires employers to keep certain records. OSHA supplies certain forms to employers available through the Internet and OSHA website. Employers with 11 or more employees must keep records of work-related illnesses and injuries.

12. **D.**

According to current statistics reported by OSHA, workplace injuries and illness rates have declined by 67 percent and occupational deaths have decreased by more than 65 percent.

13. **C.**

The Voluntary Protection Program (VPP) is used to document lost workday cases. The Alliance Program works in conjunction with several other organizations that are involved with workplace health and safety. The Challenge Program offers the opportunity for employees and employers to improve their health and safety management systems.

14. **A.**

The *chain of command* refers to the line of command that exists from the top to the bottom of an organization. The chain of command allows for a smooth exchange of information. Each subsequent layer of the chain of command must report to the one immediately above it.

15. **D.**

Approximately 48 states and the District of Columbia designate professions whose members are mandated by law to notify authorities of child and elder maltreatment. These people include:
- Social workers
- Physicians, nurses, and other healthcare workers
- Medical examiners and coroners
- Teachers, principals, and other school personnel
- Child care providers and daycare workers
- Counselors, therapists, and other mental health professionals
- Law enforcement officers

16. **D.**

The causes of health disparities include inadequate access to health care, poverty, lack of education, individual and behavioral factors, and environmental threats.

17. **A.**

Lateral violence results in damage to someone's confidence, self-esteem, or dignity. Lateral violence can consist of intentional and unintentional acts meant to intimidate, harm, or humiliate a person or group of people. This form of *harassment* puts patients and other workers at risk for poor outcomes (Rundio & Wilson, 2010).

18. **B.**

Networks allow entities to communicate, and they are a means to consolidate power, a mode for market sharing, or a way to enhance fiscal solvency through collective purchasing power. In a *decentralized system*, direct communication occurs in all directions and without restriction. With a *centralized system*, communication requires that input and output is controlled through a central point. Finally, a *restricted system* places international barriers between organizations and groups. There is no unrestricted system (Rudio & Wilson, 2010).

19. **D.**

The Computerized Medical Record System (CMRS) is a second-level product, where paper-based items are now are available electronically via scanning. The Electronic Medical Record (EMR) is a third-level product that provides capability for electronic information and data entry, data integrity, auditing, and electronic signature. The Electronic Patient Record (EPR) is a fourth-level product that brings together patient information from more than one organization or healthcare facility. The Electronic Health Record (EHR) is a fifth-level product that provides the user with information about the patient from multiple sources, including data not pertaining to his or her medical problem or health condition (Rundio & Wilson, 2010).

20. **B.**

Licensure is the mandatory process of granting permission to a person to practice in a given profession. Licensure's purpose is to protect the public from unlicensed or untrained persons. *Certification* gives recognition to nurse who meet certain requirements, generally for a particular field or clinical specialty, but it does not include a legal scope of nursing practice. *Credentialing* is the process of awarding special recognition to those who meet certain requirements. *Registration* involves board control the nursing licensure process and "register" nurses to practice under the rules and regulations of that governing body (Rundio & Wilson, 2010).

21. **C.**

The Joint Commission on the Accreditation of Hospitals (JCAH) was established in 1951, and it sets the standards for approximately 16,000 healthcare facilities in America. Joint Commission also accredits acute care hospitals, critical access facilities, medical equipment services, home healthcare and hospice agencies, rehabilitation centers, physician practices, surgical centers, skilled nursing homes, and independent laboratories.

22. **B.**

The Medicare program was aimed at the retirement age population and those with disabilities, whereas the Medicaid program was established for low income children and their parents or guardians, those with developmental disabilities, and other low income groups, such as pregnant women, the elderly, and children.

23. **C.**

The *shared governance model* allows staff nurses to be part of the decision-making process about the healthcare facility or their unit or service. In the *traditional hierarchy*, staff nurses work under a charge nurse, who works under a nurse manager, who reports to a nurse executive, and on up the chain of command. *Clinical advancement programs* (also called *career ladders* or *clinical ladders*) foster recognition of professional and expert nurses and offer a career pathway that will allow them to continue providing direct care to patients.

24. **C.**

The *functional nursing* care delivery system is a task-oriented method in which individual caregivers are not assigned to patients. The *case method nursing* care approach is often practiced in intensive care settings or in home healthcare settings. In addition to the nursing process, the RN is responsible for all indirect and direct patient care functions, and he or she communicates needs, changes, and request for assistance with a charge nurse or team leader. With *team nursing*, patients are assigned to a team of nurses, therapists, dieticians, and assistants. *Primary nursing* is a patient care system where a primary nurse is responsible for planning the patient's care and delegating tasks when he or she is not present.

25. **A.**

Credentialing is a termed used to describe the processes used for program designation when institutions or individuals have met the established standards set by an organization. <u>*Recognition* is the process where an association, organization, or agency accepts the credentialing status of another credentialing body for specified purposes. *Licensure* is the process of legal recognition of professional practice.</u>

26. **D.**

The American Nurses Association (ANA) has developed standards for nursing practice and the scope of practice. The *standards of nursing care* are guidelines for practice, which are general to any specialty or setting, and they include the broad categories of evaluation, implementation, planning, outcome identification, diagnosis, and assessment. The *standards of professional performance* address the nursing role with regard to ethics, research, education, collegiality, and resource utilization.

27. **B.**

The U.S. Nurse Practice Acts are legislations that guide and govern nursing practice. Every state has enacted a Nurse Practice Act (NPA), and their legislatures enforce the state's NPA.

28. **B.**

There are four predictable stages of *group development*: *forming,* where individuals come together and form a group; *storming,* where the group proceeds through the maturation process and identifies a leader; *norming,* where the rules of working as a group are made clear with established roles and relationships; and *performing,* where the group does most of the work and focuses energies on achieving goals.

29. **B.**

The Joint Commission (2009) mandates orientation of orient staff at hospitals with both relevant hospital-wide and unit-specific programs that both focus on policies and procedures. An orientation program can typically range from three days to four to twelve weeks, for temporary and full-time staff respectively. This length of orientation is set by the organization and should be clearly communicated to the employee.

30. **D.**

The Joint Commission standard HR.01.06.01 requires that staff *competency* be assessed and documented during orientation. One competency validation tool is the Performance Based Development System (PBDS). Many worksites accomplish *competency validation* initially via a check list. Each person's perception of their abilities varies and can skew the accuracy of these check lists.

31. **B.**

The nurse must have the ability to think critically, as well as use sound clinical judgment. *Critical thinking* is not a class that is taught, nor is it a body of knowledge learned. *Cultural competence* is the capacity for good interaction with people of different ethnicities and cultures while focusing on being personally aware of attitude regarding culture. *Leveraging diversity* is a facility's capacity for cultural competency and valuing diversity with a business and personal perspective.

32. **B.**

With intrapersonal conflict, the conflict is within oneself. With interpersonal conflict, the conflict is between the self and another person. The conflict is considered intragroup when it is among group members. Intergroup conflict is among two or more groups' members.

33. **A.**

A conceptual framework of emotional intelligence is offered by the Ability-Based Model for Emotional Intelligence. Perceiving emotions is the aptitude to identify emotions in voices, faces, and cultural artifacts and the ability to identify one's own emotional state. Using emotions is capability to promote cognitive activities with the use of emotions. Managing emotions is capability to direct one's own and others' emotions. Understanding emotions is the aptitude to understand emotional language.

34. **B.**

The level of improved health services is directly related to the desired outcomes of patients and/or patient populations and is described as quality in healthcare. A part of the Institute for Healthcare Improvement Model is the Plan-Do-Study-Act (PDSA) cycle. This is a simple tool used to accelerate quality improvement. Communication systems are formal and informal structures used to support the communication needs within an organization.

35. **B.**

Systems are either closed or open. *Closed systems* occur only in physical sciences, such as the circulatory system. *Open systems* interact with the environment and internally. The parts of this system are input, throughput, and output.

36. **D.**

With active listening, the listener repeats back what they hear to the speaker to confirm understanding between both parties. Reflective communication involves working to understand the idea of the speaker, and an offer to support the speaker's idea in an attempt to reconstruct the idea and relay understanding. Two-way communication is a form of transmission in which both parties transmit information, such as chatrooms, instant messaging, telephone conversations, and in-person discussions. An interview is a conversation between two or more people, which is done in medial reporting, in qualitative research, in employee statements, and to receive the facts.

37. **D.**

One preferred style of communication is the persuasive style. This style encourages others to view ideas as beneficial to their needs, displays authority to build trust, and reassures staff by creating an emotive and empathetic connection. The assertive communication style involves standing up for personal rights and expressing feelings, beliefs, and thoughts in an honest, direct, and appropriate way which does not violate another individual's rights. It is also a preferred communication style. The passive style involves violating your own rights by failing to express your feelings, beliefs, and thoughts and allowing others to violate your rights, and it is not preferred.

38. **C.**

The goal of RCA is to identify both active and latent errors, those that are hidden. *Benchmarking* is a technique that identifies top quality as a means of comparing one's practice or healthcare facility with those who are judged objectively to be the standard or pacesetter of a certain category. *Report cards* are issued by accrediting bodies, such as payers or The Joint Commission. Functional areas within an organization must accurately perform the work for which they are accountable so that the organization can achieve goals and surpass competitors. The *functional status* of an organization involves areas that are interdependent.

39. **D.**

Sentinel events are unexpected occurrences that have the potential to result in or actually cause death or injury. *Nursing sensitive indicators* are associated with the process, structure, and outcomes of nursing care. *Structure indicators* measure the supply of nursing staff, the staff member's skill level, and the education and certification of nursing staff. *Process indicators* measure nursing care aspects, for example intervention and assessment. *Outcome indicators* are specific to patient outcomes or quality of nursing care, such as intravenous infiltrations or falls.

40. **C.**

Continuous quality improvement (CQI) is the process of continually increasing quality. *Performance improvement* (PI) activities are those that involve the quality structure of most healthcare facilities and medical organizations. *Total quality management* (TQM) is the process where everyone employed by the healthcare facility is committed to continuous improvement. There are many *stakeholders* with vested interests in a healthcare organization, such as the patient and family, the staff, the physicians, and the payers. Stakeholder satisfaction is when these persons approve of the healthcare organization.

41. **C.**

ORYX indicators are part of the accreditation process that integrates outcomes and other performance improvement data. ORYX measurement requirements support healthcare facilities accredited by Joint Commission in their effort to improve quality. *Structure indicators* measure the supply of nursing staff, the staff member's skill level, and the education and certification of nursing staff. *Process indicators* measure nursing care aspects, for example intervention and assessment. *Outcome indicators* are specific to patient outcomes or quality of nursing care, such as intravenous infiltrations or falls.

42. **B.**

These statements are meant to motivate and inspire those who are affiliated with the healthcare facility, and they are future-oriented and address what the facility plans to do give its resources. Most of these involve statements about the staff and administration.

43. **D.**

Organizations are structured in several ways. In a joint venture, one partner provides a service, and the other partner provides financing. With the vertical integration model, there is different but complementary services available to all parties, such as the affiliation with a HMO and a hospital. In horizontal integration, services are shared across two or more organizations, such as the provision of oncology services by one and the provision of orthopedic services by the other. Shared governance fosters ownership of work that is done by involvement of workers in decisions about staffing, performance, structure, and resource allocation.

44. **B.**

The *contingency plan* is the way the healthcare facility operates on a day-to-day basis, and it includes adverse events. *Strategic planning* is the development of an organizational strategy that will provide a long-term road map for a healthcare facility. *Program planning* is the organization's capacity to successfully execute a plan or service. With this process, the programs must match the organization's philosophy and beliefs to create a profit for the healthcare facility. A culture of collaborative accountability, practice, and communication comprises a healthy work environment is.

45. **C.**

Servant leaders put other people and their needs before their own and choose to lead by serving the interests of others. Charismatic leaders have the ability to engage others with the power of their personalities, and they inspire emotional connection and use charisma to advance revolutionary ideas. Connective leaders draw on their ability to bring others together to facilitate change. Transactional leaders associate with the principles of social-exchange theory, which implies that social, psychological, and political benefits exist in all relationships, such as that of the leader and follower.

46. **D.**

Permissive leaders have a lot of faith in their subordinates, assuming they can make good decisions and need little direction. Autocratic leaders attempt to change the behavior of subordinates through external control by coercion, punishment, authority, and power. Democratic leaders focus on changing subordinates through participation, involvement in goal setting, and collaboration. Bureaucratic leaders rely on the healthcare facility policies and rules to control and influence subordinates.

47. **C.**

Lewin proposed that people maintain a state of equilibrium, and for this to occur, there must be a disruption of balance. To lessen the power of restraining forces, one must either increase the force or decrease the power of the force. With *Maslow's Hierarchy of Needs Theory*, there are five elementary life necessities that are common to all people, and the hierarchy is an arrangement that ranks the concepts from lowest to highest. To achieve success, the person must meet the needs at the lower levels before he or she tackles the next levels. The *Herzberg's Two-Factor Theory* states defined the specific workplace factors that contribute to job satisfaction and also another factor set that leads to dissatisfaction. *Rogers' Change Theory* holds that innovations perceived by people that could have greater advantage for change should be adopted more rapidly than other innovations.

48. **B.**

Strategic planning is the development of an organizational strategy that will provide a long-term road map for a healthcare facility. *Succession planning* is part of strategic planning. *Contingency planning* the way the healthcare facility operates on a day-to-day basis, and it involves preparation for adverse events. *Program planning* is the organization's capacity to successfully execute a plan or service.

49. **B.**

Case study research involves investigation of a single individual or a group with similar diagnoses. Applied research is designed to solve a practical problem or answer a question. Descriptive research reports selected variables and proves facts that already are accepted. Experimental research randomly assigns participants with manipulation of variables.

50. **A.**

Field research is conducted in the natural setting. Historical research explains or interprets something in the past. Laboratory research is conducted in a setting designed for research. Longitudinal research involves measuring the same participants as they grow older.

51. **C.**

The *institutional review boards* (IRBs) exist to ensure that research participants are protected from unscrupulous and unethical practices and researchers. Guidance documents are posted on the FDA website and these guidelines show the FDA's opinions on the best ways protect human research subjects. Second level grant applications review and recommendations for application approval and consideration are offered by the National Advisory Council for Nursing Research (NACNR) provides. *Nursing research councils* educate nurses about the importance of using research in clinical practice.

52. **B.**

Data is either qualitative or quantitative. *Qualitative data* involves the use of words to describe concepts, facts, participants' statements, and subjective observations. *Quantitative data* involves the use of numbers to enhance study precision. Three categories of quantitative data are: nominal data, which cannot be arranged in any particular order, such as marital status, religion, and race; ordinal data, which are ordered, but differences cannot be determined, such as socioeconomic status, car size, and facility ratings; and interval data, which are ordered and have meaningful differences, such as ratio data where there is an absolute zero.

53. **A.**

Validity means that the data-gathering instrument measures exactly what it is meant to measure. *Reliability* is how well or how consistent an instrument is for the purpose of a particular study. While an instrument may be able to measure something time and time again(reliable) without being appropriate (valid), an instrument may not be valid unless it is both reliable and valid.

54. **B.**

The eight dimensions of strategic innovation are: the managed innovation process, which combines strategic approaches of a traditional and non-traditional nature; strategic alignment, which acquires support internally; industry foresight, which helps understand rising trends; patient insight, which helps understand unarticulated and articulated patient needs; core technologies and competencies, which involves using corporate assets as leverage; organizational readiness, which involves the capacity to act; disciplined implementation, which inspiration to impact business, which is a platform for ongoing competitive advantage.

55. **B.**

The *divergence phase* is strategic innovation's center; possesses traits of exploration, open-endedness, inquisitiveness; and entails the use of creative thought and techniques that envision the future. The *convergence phase* involves conventional development and planning for business, where opportunities are selected, assessed, cultivated, and executed. There is no emergence phase.

56. **E.**

The Equal Employment Opportunity Commission (EEOC) enforces equal employment laws involve various aspects of discrimination due to color, race, religion, age, national origin, sex, pregnancy, sexual orientation, and sexual harassment.

57. **D.**

With the Workers' Compensation law, an employee who is injured or becomes ill on the job or from a condition caused by the worksite, is compensated for that incident. Workers' compensation is payment for permanent injury (not minor injury), costs of rehabilitation, a percentage of wages or salary, and absolute liability for medical coverage.

58. **C.**

Collective bargaining is an agreement negotiated between an employer and a labor union that sets forth the terms of employment for workers who are members of that labor union. The term "collective" shows that agreements cover a defined population within an organization and are not individualized. A *grievance* is any complaint made by the involved parties. *Arbitration* is a process where a final and binding award is given by an arbitrator. A *contract* is a legally qualified agreement for a particular benefit of two or more people, which is a voluntary act.

59. **D.**

A *contract* is a legally qualified agreement for a particular benefit of two or more people, which is a voluntary act. Many states accept verbal contracts as legal contracts under this concept.

60. **B.**

Lateral thinking (also called innovative thinking) creates the idea, while vertical thinking (also called logical thinking) moves the idea forward. Critical thinking is the ability to analyzed a situation and use past knowledge to make decisions that are sound and fact-based.

61. **D.**

The fee for service payment method involves a set price for a service. With healthcare, the amount paid for services is often negotiated between the provider and the payer. With the *pay for performance* (PFP) approach, the healthcare insurer or other payer pays healthcare facilities and physicians based on performance. The *pay for coordination* (PFC) payment applies to specified care coordination services by certain types of providers, such as home healthcare. With the *bundled payment* method, the services delivered by two or more providers during a single care episode over a certain period of time is covered with a single, bundled payment.

62. **A.**

The hours per patient day (HPPD) is the total hours of nursing care that must be provided per patient per day. By dividing total production hours by the number of patients, HPPD is determined.

63. **B.**

Part of the capital budgeting process is *amortization*, an assignment of costs to a capital item for its lifetime. This considers critically important aspects of the "life expectancy" of an item, which allows room for development of a replacement strategy. When revenue and expense segments are separated, an operating budget, allows for easily calculating loss or profit. The *average daily census* measures inpatient volume based on the number of occupied beds or number of patients.

64. **B.**

Healthy People provides Americans with science-based, 10-year national objectives for improving health of all age groups. Healthy People 2020 reflects input from a diverse group of individuals and organizations and is a 10-year agenda to improve the health of the nation. Objectives include increased public awareness of the determinants of health, disability, and disease, provision of goals and objectives that are applicable at the local, state, and national levels, and identification of critical research, data collection, and evaluation needs.

65. **D.**

According to the Agency for Healthcare Research and Quality (2013c), numerous health disparities were found in a recent report. These include: Blacks, American Indians, Asians, Native Alaskans, and Hispanics received worse care than Whites; poor or low income people did not receive the quality of care of high income individuals; Blacks, Asians, Hispanics, Native Americans, and Native Alaskans all had worse access to care than Whites; poor people had worse care access than high income people; in 2005, Americans did not receive one third of the healthcare services needed; and in 2002, 24 percent of Americans had difficulties finding access to health care, and by 2009, this had increased to 26 percent.

66. **D.**

The Affordable Care Act called for the establishment of the Patient-Centered Outcomes Research Institute, which studies comparative effectiveness research that is funded by a fee on those insured. It also allows the FDA to approve generic drugs, with 12 years of exclusive use for new biologic medications. Additionally, this law involves programs that increase incentives to provide collaborative and quality healthcare.

67. **B.**

The Whistleblower Protection Act of 1989 protects federal whistleblowers who work for the government and report misconduct of an organization or agency. Whistleblowers can file complaints that they believe constitute a violation of: a rule, regulation, or law; gross mismanagement; gross waste of funds; abuse of authority; or a substantial, specific danger to public safety and health. The Health Insurance Portability and Accountability Act (HIPPA) of 1996 is a law that involves the electronic exchange and protection of healthcare information and patient data. The Fair Labor Standards Act (FLSA) establishes minimum wage, record keeping, overtime pay, and young employment standards for full-time and part-time workers in the private sector and in local, state, and federal governments. Under the Civil Rights Act, employers cannot discriminate against an employee based on factors not related to job qualifications, such as age, sexual preference, religion, race, sex, or national origin.

68. **A.**

The Centers for Medicare and Medicaid Services (CMS) partnered with the Agency for Healthcare Research and Quality (AHRQ) to develop HCAHPS. These two Department of Health and Human Service organizations developed an initiative to provide a standardized survey instrument and data collection methodology for measuring patients' perspectives on hospital care.

69. **C.**

In a *decentralized system*, direct communication occurs in all directions and without restriction. With a *centralized system*, communication requires that input and output is controlled through a central point. A *local area network* (LAN) is several personal computers linked together through a server, and it allows for communication among organization personnel. A *wide area network* (WAN) is a system that is made of many LANs, where connections are affected by specialized networking software.

70. **A.**

Nurse compact legislation is a growing trend that is endorsed in most states, and model legislative language exists for licensure recognition. The *nurse compact* implies that state agencies must give up certain measures of parochial control of practice within their regions.

Exclusive Trivium Test Tips

Here at Trivium Test Prep, we strive to offer you the exemplary test tools that help you pass your exam the first time. This book includes an overview of important concepts, example questions throughout the text, and practice test questions. But we know that learning how to successfully take a test can be just as important as learning the content being tested. In addition to excelling on the Nurse Exec, we want to give you the solutions you need to be successful every time you take a test. Our study strategies, preparation pointers, and test tips will help you succeed as you take the Nurse Exec and any test in the future!

Study Strategies

1. Spread out your studying. By taking the time to study a little bit every day, you strengthen your understanding of the testing material, so it's easier to recall that information on the day of the test. Our study guides make this easy by breaking up the concepts into sections with example practice questions, so you can test your knowledge as you read.
2. Create a study calendar. The sections of our book make it easy to review and practice with example questions on a schedule. Decide to read a specific number of pages or complete a number of practice questions every day. Breaking up all of the information in this way can make studying less overwhelming and more manageable.
3. Set measurable goals and motivational rewards. Follow your study calendar and reward yourself for completing reading, example questions, and practice problems and tests. You could take yourself out after a productive week of studying or watch a favorite show after reading a chapter. Treating yourself to rewards is a great way to stay motivated.
4. Use your current knowledge to understand new, unfamiliar concepts. When you learn something new, think about how it relates to something you know really well. Making connections between new ideas and your existing understanding can simplify the learning process and make the new information easier to remember.
5. Make learning interesting! If one aspect of a topic is interesting to you, it can make an entire concept easier to remember. Stay engaged and think about how concepts covered on the exam can affect the things you're interested in. The sidebars throughout the text offer additional information that could make ideas easier to recall.
6. Find a study environment that works for you. For some people, absolute silence in a library results in the most effective study session, while others need the background noise of a coffee shop to fuel productive studying. There are many websites that generate white noise and recreate the sounds of different environments for studying. Figure out what distracts you and what engages you and plan accordingly.
7. Take practice tests in an environment that reflects the exam setting. While it's important to be as comfortable as possible when you study, practicing taking the test exactly as you'll take it on test day will make you more prepared for the actual exam. If your test starts on a Saturday morning, take your practice test on a Saturday morning. If you have access, try to find an empty classroom that has desks like the desks at testing center. The more closely you can mimic the testing center, the more prepared you'll feel on test day.
8. Study hard for the test in the days before the exam, but take it easy the night before and do something relaxing rather than studying and cramming. This will help decrease anxiety, allow you to get a better night's sleep, and be more mentally fresh during the big exam. Watch a light-hearted movie, read a favorite book, or take a walk, for example.

Preparation Pointers

1. Preparation is key! Don't wait until the day of your exam to gather your pencils, calculator, identification materials, or admission tickets. Check the requirements of the exam as soon as possible. Some tests require materials that may take more time to obtain, such as a passport-style photo, so be sure that you have plenty of time to collect everything. The night before the exam, lay out everything you'll need, so it's all ready to go on test day! We recommend at least two forms of ID, your admission ticket or confirmation, pencils, a high protein, compact snack, bottled water, and any necessary medications. Some testing centers will require you to put all of your supplies in a clear plastic bag. If you're prepared, you will be less stressed the morning of, and less likely to forget anything important.
2. If you're taking a pencil-and-paper exam, test your erasers on paper. Some erasers leave big, dark stains on paper instead of rubbing out pencil marks. Make sure your erasers work for you and the pencils you plan to use.
3. Make sure you give yourself your usual amount of sleep, preferably at least 7 – 8 hours. You may find you need even more sleep. Pay attention to how much you sleep in the days before the exam, and how many hours it takes for you to feel refreshed. This will allow you to be as sharp as possible during the test and make fewer simple mistakes.
4. Make sure to make transportation arrangements ahead of time, and have a backup plan in case your ride falls through. You don't want to be stressing about how you're going to get to the testing center the morning of the exam.
5. Many testing locations keep their air conditioners on high. You want to remember to bring a sweater or jacket in case the test center is too cold, as you never know how hot or cold the testing location could be. Remember, while you can always adjust for heat by removing layers, if you're cold, you're cold.

Test Tips

1. Go with your gut when choosing an answer. Statistically, the answer that comes to mind first is often the right one. This is assuming you studied the material, of course, which we hope you have done if you've read through one of our books!
2. For true or false questions: if you genuinely don't know the answer, mark it true. In most tests, there are typically more true answers than false answers.
3. For multiple-choice questions, read ALL the answer choices before marking an answer, even if you think you know the answer when you come across it. You may find your original "right" answer isn't necessarily the best option.
4. Look for key words: in multiple choice exams, particularly those that require you to read through a text, the questions typically contain key words. These key words can help the test taker choose the correct answer or confuse you if you don't recognize them. Common keywords are: *most, during, after, initially,* and *first.* Be sure you identify them before you read the available answers. Identifying the key words makes a huge difference in your chances of passing the test.
5. Narrow answers down by using the process of elimination: after you understand the question, read each answer. If you don't know the answer right away, use the process of elimination to narrow down the answer choices. It is easy to identify at least one answer that isn't correct. Continue to narrow down the choices before choosing the answer you believe best fits the question. By following this process, you increase your chances of selecting the correct answer.

6.   Don't worry if others finish before or after you. Go at your own pace, and focus on the test in front of you.

7.   Relax. With our help, we know you'll be ready to conquer the Nurse Exec. You've studied and worked hard!

Keep in mind that every individual takes tests differently, so strategies that might work for you may not work for someone else. You know yourself best and are the best person to determine which of these tips and strategies will benefit your studying and test taking. Best of luck as you study, test, and work toward your future!

Made in the USA
Middletown, DE
21 September 2017